"*Food Plague* is an apt description of circumstances slowly encompassing us. The conditions in our soils, crops, barns, and homes are not normal and are precipitating a health crisis seldom experienced in history. Dr. Andersen examines the causes, and provides a commonsense, straightforward approach to begin the healing process through the selection of nutrient-dense food and avoidance of the GMO/glyphosate entrapment that is depriving us of the nutrients and biological environment that are basic to our physical, behavioral, and mental health. He identifies the concerns, their causes, and the practical solutions needed to change. Dr. Andersen's basic, practical approach outlined in *Food Plague* provides a direct approach to restore the nutritional density and balance that is essential for a long, happy, and productive life."

— Don M. Huber, Ph.D., Professor Emeritus,
Purdue University.

"During the last thirty-seven years as a clinical pharmacist and a clinical nutritionist, I have observed the degradation in health of my patients and Americans at the hands of our food supplies. Not only is what we eat, even the organically grown varieties, grossly depleted of nutrients, it is replete with genetically modified crops and poisons that short circuit our biochemistry, leading to toxic dysfunction and illness. The science of how this happens is known but ignored and even covered up for the sake of money. The makers of these products lie to themselves, the farmers, the USDA, the FDA, healthcare providers, and the public as the safety and "benefits" of their creations. Collateral fallout is assumed, planned on, and accepted by these companies and the government officials that authorize their use. I beg my patients to avoid these Frankenfoods, as their health is in peril should they not heed the years of warnings.

Finally here is a volume, written by a physician and agronomist, that focuses on the cost to our health and in healthcare dollars of GMOs and the ubiquitously used Round-Up, written in a way that consumers and healthcare professionals can understand and become empowered to make changes not only in their own lives, but in the policies of our country. Dr. Andersen does present solutions to our food plague crisis that are reasonable and doable now, leaving us with hope for a more toxin free, nutritious future. It is up to us."

— Lisa Everett, B.Sc. Pharm, FACA, CCN

Food Plague

Could Our Daily Bread Be Our Most Life-threatening Exposure?

Arden Andersen, D.O., M.S.P.H., Ph.D.

Holographic Press

Waynesville, NC 28785

Books available from Crossroads Healing Arts,
574-875-4227.

ISBN: 978-0-9893264-1-4

My thanks and appreciation to Dr. Don Huber, Professor Emeritus Purdue University and Colonel U.S. Army (Ret.), for his tireless quest for truth, science, and most importantly "truth in science." Had it not been for his work, teaching, and presentation, much of this information would still be locked away from public awareness. Thank you to Michele, Beth, and Pola Firestone with her team at BookWorks for their enthusiastic assistance in editing and revising.

About the Author

Arden Andersen is uniquely trained as both a holistic physician and a soil and crop consultant. He holds a bachelor of science degree in agriculture from the University of Arizona; a master of science degree in public health from the University of South Florida, Tampa, Florida; a doctorate of osteopathic medicine from Western University of Health Sciences, Pomona, California; and a Ph.D. in agricultural biophysics from Clayton University, St. Louis, Missouri. He is residency trained in occupational medicine, board certified in public health and prolotherapy, and a certified cenegenics trained physician.

He has traveled the world to teach soil and crop nutrition and consult biological fertilizer and farm management companies seeking to produce nutrient dense, high-brix foods. He was invited to speak by the Ministry of Agriculture and Ministry of Trade of South Africa at the annual allFresh Conference. He has testified in front of the New Zealand Parliamentary

Committee on Agriculture, the New South Wales Shadow Committee on Agriculture, and the committee assessing approval of GMO crops in Victoria, Australia. He has consulted small and large farming operations in North and South America, Australia, New Zealand, South Africa, Europe, and the British Isles. His book, *The Anatomy of Life and Energy in Agriculture*, published in 1989, brought the concept of nutrient-dense food to the discussion table. In 2012, he was awarded the Eco-Agriculture Lifetime Achievement Award. While many people talk about food quality from a philosophical perspective, Dr. Andersen grounds it in the scientific arena where food quality relates to actual nutrient density or quantity of minerals, vitamins, antioxidants, and plant secondary metabolites with its direct correlation to human health and environmental regeneration.

His medical practice is both an extension of and the foundation for his agricultural teaching and consultation. It is nutritionally based incorporating the best of conventional and alternative medicine along with environmental and occupational health connections. He was nominated for the *Grand Rapids* Magazine Medicine Hall of Fame in 2000. His medical practice includes a distinctive career as a flight surgeon in the U.S. Air Force Reserve. When he speaks about nutrition and food quality, he speaks not only as a nutritionally based physician but as an expert in actually producing that food. He has written many articles on the subjects of health and agriculture. Dr. Andersen has recorded numerous CDs and video seminars. His books include *Real Medicine, Real Health, Science in Agriculture, The Anatomy of Life and Energy in Agriculture*, and *Applied Body Electronics*. His most recent, *Food Plague*, elegantly and realistically links modern food to human suffering and illness. *Food Plague* exemplifies Dr. Andersen's extensive and multifaceted understanding of health at all levels.

Table of Contents

Foreword...xi

Introduction 1

Chapter 1:
Health, Pre-Disease, and Disease 7

Chapter 2:
Nature Knows Best...13

Chapter 3:
Genetic Engineering 35

Chapter 4:
Genetic Roulette: Science Proves GMOs To Be Toxic.....55

Chapter 5:
The Human Connection..69

Chapter 6:
Horizontal Gene Transfer and Viral Wildcats.................73

Chapter 7:
The GMO Trend..77

Chapter 8:
The Deadly Bedfellow of GM Crops 87

Chapter 9:
An Emerging Disease Agent 115

Chapter 10:
The Modern Agricultural Complex: Concocter of the
"Green Revolution" 125

Chapter 11:
Food Quality and Bricks.....................................137

Chapter 12:
... and the Rest of the Story 155

Chapter 13:
It's in the Water 157

Chapter 14:
Antibiotics and Growth Hormones 161

Chapter 15:
Environmental Consequences and Sustainability 175

Chapter 16:
Organic v. Not Organic 187

Chapter 17:
Grass-fed v. Grain-fed 197

Chapter 18:
Wild v. Farm Raised Fish 203

Chapter 19:
A1 v. A2 Milk 207

Chapter 20:
Pesticides and Endocrine Disruptors 213

Chapter 21:
Sanitation, Pathogens, and Parasites 227

Chapter 22:
Recommendations 233

Chapter 23:
The Solutions: "The Kitchen Gardener" 239

The Food We Eat 265

APPENDIX 269

Foreword

There are core issues that I believe are defining problems for the future of our society. These are the declining nutrient values of our food, genetic engineering of our foods and its collateral damage, and the emerging invasive biomolecular matrix consequent to the first two core issues. There are then a number of peripheral food health and safety issues, including antibiotics and growth hormones, pesticides and endocrine disruptors, A1 versus A2 milk, wild versus farm-raised fish, grass-fed versus grain-fed beef, organic versus not organic foods, sanitation, pathogens and parasites, and finally the environmental consequences of the "modern" agricultural industry.

Certainly, all this information, well documented in the scientific literature, can be quite disheartening or downright depressing, even frightening. If one is simply left with that information, he or she would feel lost for what to do, how to respond, how to live a healthy life. In physics, there is the principle that for every force there is an equal and opposite force. With that in mind, I will disperse throughout this book and conclude with the counter force, which is fundamentally about nutrition, of true sustainability—sustainability that actually does sustain the Earth and every living creature, including humans, indefinitely. Nature provides the rules and the means for such sustainability if one just learns the rules and abides by their enforcement. Nature is truly our teacher and our protector in this endeavor. Nature is also the great cleanser, sending ever stronger forces to clear out defects and aberrations in living systems from diseases to insect pests, droughts to floods. The longer we choose to remain outside of her rules, the greater and more violent will be the battle.

The Omnivore's Dilemma by Michael Pollan and *The Maker's Diet* by Jordan Rubin are great places to start reading about diet and health. *Food Plague* looks deeper into the whys and wherefores of food and health and the underlying issues that make food what it is or is not. Healthcare providers and consumers alike need to be more than just on board with the latest in diet, exercise and lifestyle. The best paleo or low-glycemic diet in the world is no better than the quality of the foods that went into the animals and/or the quality of the soil that grows the animal's foods and the fruits and vegetables the consumer eats. Physicians, nutritionists, and consumers need to know what is behind food quality or toxicity, and that simply having food that is certified organic, biodynamic, naturally grown, or grass-fed does not guarantee the product is nutritionally sound, clean, or healthful.

Further, urban and suburban consumers apply more pesticides per land area than do farmers in the name of green lawns and weed-free sidewalks, not to mention the household insecticides and landscape algaecides applied *carte blanche*. Healthcare professionals and consumers alike need to know that there are viable nontoxic options that actually result in prettier landscapes, more resilient and economical lawns and turf, all without the environmental or ill health consequences. As such, I will explain some of the basic science behind insect, microorganism, and weed behavior; why are they here, what do they mean, and how do we correct them. Your lawn, lake, and garden are not pesticide deficient, they are nutrient deficient.

Food Plague addresses these issues and more, giving the consumer the knowledge and resources to make a difference in their own health as well as the overall industry via their votes at the grocery store.

Introduction

Food is medicine, good or bad. Like all medicines, where there are differences in the quality of synthesis, the specific molecular tweaking correlating to why one medicine works better or poorer than another medicine for the same malady, so, too, foods vary considerably in their quality of growing, nutrient value, digestibility, assimilability, their satiation value, their medicinal value, and what potential side effects they carry. This book is intended to help the reader see food for what it is: sustenance; for what it is supposed to do for the consumer: supply nutrition; and food's potential dark side as a deadly killer.

Historically, the only potential dark side to food was inadvertently getting a potentially poisonous plant, such as a mushroom or berry; getting a contaminating organism due to poor food preservation; or having a rare but serious anaphylactic allergic reaction, such as with peanuts. Today, we have a much more complex and deceiving danger in our food chain.

Like the 1973 movie *Soylent Green*, all is not well nor truthfully revealed regarding our "modern" food supply.

This is not a philosophy book to promote one political agenda or the other. This book is about science and the facts that modern agriculture has so lost its way, has so lost its understanding that food production is necessary for the sustainment of life on this planet, has so lost its appreciation that Nature holds the keys to real abundant and healthful food production that food has become potentially our most life-threatening exposure. Modern agriculture has abandoned science in favor of private agenda.

Further, this book is about exposing the truth of the worldwide poisoning of our food chain, water, soil, environment, and people; that this poisoning has created dangerous new diseases and infective agents and further depleted the nutrient value of the food. Infertility, spontaneous abortions, miscarriages, birth defects, behavioral problems, irritable bowel, food sensitivities, resistant infections, autism, and cancer are the true scourges left in the wake of "modern agriculture."

There are many topics to cover regarding health, food quality, and longevity. Fundamentally, the most important aspect is nutrition; specifically, what vitamins, minerals, amino acids, proteins, fatty acids, antioxidants, and phytonutrients will the food provide. Unfortunately, most people, especially doctors, turn to dieticians for "nutritional" information and advice.

Dieticians are trained in the art of fats, proteins, and carbohydrates; balancing energy, following the USDA contrived food pyramid, which only guarantees the sale of more junk agricultural commodities and perpetuation of human suffering and disease.

Hospital dietary plans are a good example of what not to eat. Nutrition is what needs to be addressed; specifically, that which is contained in the food coming off the farm. Everything else is secondary to the nutrient value of the food because the body's ability to function properly, fully, in a healthy state is determined by what nutrition is taken in by the body.

Certainly there are concerns for pesticide and chemical residues, toxic metals, and pathogens; however, the body's ability to deal with these assaults is entirely determined by the comprehensiveness of the nutrition taken in via the food and supplementation. Consequently, first and foremost in any discussion about health, lifestyle, dietary or food plans, exercise, and hormone/metabolic balancing is food nutritional value followed by overall food quality. Next, the discussion about "genetically engineered foods and their collateral damage." Third on the list of core food topics would be the deadly infective biomolecular matrix thanks to genetic engineering, glyphosate/RoundUp and demineralization. Truly the combination of food demineralization, genetically engineered "Frankenfoods", glyphosate, and an infective biomolecular matrix is the 21st Century Plague.

More peripheral yet important topics in the table of contents include antibiotics and growth hormones in food; pesticides and endocrine disruptors; environmental consequences and sustainability; A1 versus A2 milk; organic versus not organic; grass-fed versus grain-fed animals; sanitation, pathogens (including BSE), and parasites; leaky gut and inflammation; and, finally, what to do about all of this nonsense?

God said that My people perish for the lack of knowledge. It has never been truer than today.

I will not leave the reader in the lurch or depressed state of hopelessness about our current Food Plague. The plague is correctable, curable, and reversible, and as such, I will leave the reader with solutions because we have the technology, the knowledge, the experience, the science, everything we need to solve all these problems. By default, we solve the greenhouse gas debate, the starvation issue, the pest problems, and environmental issues. Oh, by the way, did I mention we are already doing it, quietly, decisively, deliberately and unimpeded here in the U.S. and around the world? That's how I can so assuredly state what I have stated. We are the grassroots movement.

Chapter 1

Health, Pre-Disease, and Disease

Our bodies are complex organisms, electrical in nature, consisting of trillions of cells made up of at least eighty different minerals, thousands of different proteins, fatty acids, organic acids, lipids, sugars, and, of course, water. Our cells undergo billions (yes billions with a "b") atomic and molecular reactions every second. The efficiency and effectiveness of these reactions depend upon the adequacy and balance of all the nutrients involved, directly and indirectly. One missing or inadequately supplied nutrient disrupts the entire metabolic factory or, worst case, can shut down entire metabolic pathways. Such a shutdown occurs with deficiencies of mineral and vitamin cofactors, such as selenium, iodine, zinc, manganese, copper, and iron. A slight diversion is in order at this time.

Health and disease are relative terms and relative states of being. Some people, especially doctors, would say something to the effect, "Other than Mrs. Smith's metastatic breast cancer, she is in perfect health." That is an oxymoron. The very fact that Mrs. Smith has metastatic breast cancer means she is a long way from perfect health. Diseases are not separate from our state of health. They are a manifestation of our state of health.

I will define my scale of health and disease. Draw a vertical line with 0 at the bottom and 100 at the top. Zero is death and 100 is perfect health. Divide the line into three sections. The top section is labeled "healthy," the middle section is labeled "pre-disease," and the bottom section is labeled "disease." Disease is defined as having any diagnosed or yet to be diagnosed malady whether it be terminal, infective, parasitic, or genetic. This would include cancer, heart disease, diabetes, obesity, Crohn's disease, irritable bowel syndrome (IBS), arthritis, and so on. Medicine today is totally focused on disease: predicting it, searching for it, identifying it, naming it, and then attacking it. "Search and destroy" is the modus operandi. Medicine has perfected the "search and destroy" methodology. Unfortunately, searching out, naming, and destroying disease does not grant us nor leave us with health. It leaves us where we were prior to the disease diagnosis, at pre-disease or, worse, dead.

The U.S. medical machine accounts for over 240,000 deaths per year, over 100,000 of those directly due to prescription medications. Medicine is the third leading cause of death in the U.S., statistically speaking. Actually, it is the fourth leading cause because heart disease and cancer are both significantly attributable to agriculture making agriculture the number one killer in America.

Pre-disease is the state of being susceptible to any of the myriad of diagnoses not yet "caught up to the person." This means that the body's immune system is compromised to the point that if one is exposed to an infective agent, the infective agent has and gets the upper hand. It means that the body is in a state of insufficient nutrition to maintain health, to ward off infection and aberrant cellular activity. It is a transition state between health and disease either in the direction of decline or rebuilding. Pre-disease is a very profitable status for the medical profession, second only to disease in profitability.

Pre-disease is often labeled as "health" by the medical community because the medical community is focused like a laser on disease, and unless a disease can be identified, the patient is determined to be "healthy" until proven disease strikes like a thief in the night. It's a thrilling action drama of "search and destroy" missions in real life.

Health is the state of being fully alive more than just free of disease. It is a state where the body functions to the maximum capability undaunted by exposures to dastardly creepy-crawlers lurking around every corner, undaunted by the rigors of life and offenses of man-made chemistry. Can we achieve such a state of life here on planet Earth in the 21st century? I think we can come very close if not outright achieve it, but only with the right ammunition, the right and adequate nutrition, along with the appropriate spiritual maturity.

Perfection/Ascension

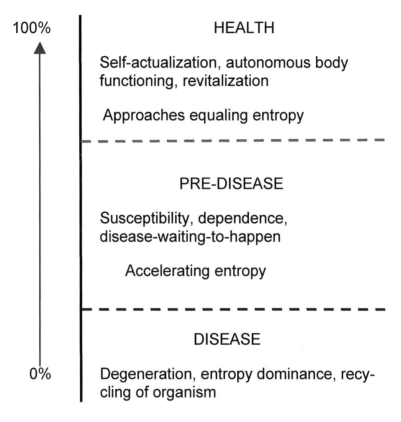

100%   HEALTH

Self-actualization, autonomous body
functioning, revitalization

Approaches equaling entropy

PRE-DISEASE

Susceptibility, dependence,
disease-waiting-to-happen

Accelerating entropy

DISEASE

0%   Degeneration, entropy dominance, recycling of organism

Death/Recycling

As one achieves improving nutrition, one moves up on the
scale; with diminishing nutrition one moves down on the
scale.

Chapter 2

Nature Knows Best

The functioning of Nature, although complex, is fairly straightforward and matter of fact. Survival of the fittest is a metaphor we use often to depict Nature as ruthless, unyielding, frightening, and even arrogant. However, survival of the fittest, taken in pure natural science, outside of the political arena, is about maintaining healthy descendants adapted to and capable of surviving the elements of the environment in which Nature places us. Sickly, weak, nutritionally deficient organisms cannot "weather the storm" of our environment. Nature has put in place means to recycle the components of all organisms so to maintain the fittest. These include parasites, which are simply Nature's garbage recycling crew; disease organisms—bacteria, fungi, and viruses—which also are garbage recycling workers at the microscopic level.

Our bodies are more exogenous microorganisms than endogenous cells. In other words, there are more microorganisms colonizing our body, inside and out, than cells that constitute our body itself. These microorganisms maintain our body, protect it from invasion from nonsymbiotic organisms, help digest our food, manufacture vital nutrients, and really make us what we are physically. The things we apply to our body, the foods we eat, beverages we drink, and supplements we ingest all determine the characteristics of this exogenous "body." It will be as effective at its tasks as is its "health" determined by what microorganisms predominate. This exogenous "body of microorganisms" is where our state of health, pre-disease, and disease begin.

These microorganisms need a full complement of nutrients to do their job. Any alteration in the spectrum and quality of this nutrient supply alters what microorganisms survive and dominate our body surfaces. Most medical workers recognize distinctive odors of people having specific diseases, e.g., diabetes and cancer. Remember, environment determines who lives and dies. Environment determines genetic expression.

Over a century ago, Gunther Enderlin, a renowned microbiologist competitor of Louis Pasteur, emphasized that the terrain was the key more so than the organism isolated because a change in the terrain, changed what organisms would be isolated. That, of course, is common sense today as microbiologists know that they must use certain growth medium to elicit the growth of specific microorganisms. One cannot grow out *mycobacterium tuberculosis* under the same conditions or on the same growth medium as one can grow *streptococcus* or *E. coli* or *lactobacillus*. Well, our diet and lifestyle determine the macroscopic and microscopic environment/terrain of our body, inside and out.

The phrase "you are what you eat" takes on great meaning. Actually, "you are what you feed your body microorganisms." That microbial food is your diet, the food or junk with which you fill your belly. Unfortunately in our current world of deniability, complete lack of personal responsibility and contention of entitlement, people seek to blame anything and everything other than themselves for their plight in life and their personal health or disease. "Bad genes" or "unfortunate luck of the draw" are the excuses ignorantly or lazily espoused by many doctors, parroted by unscrupulous biotech researchers with dollar signs in their eyes, and gladly accepted by consumers so to justify their lack of taking personal responsibility for their health and, to further justify their "en-

titlement" to "free healthcare." It's one's diet and lifestyle
that causes the "bad genes" in the first place so there is no
getting around the personal responsibility of every person for
his own health . . . with one caveat.

The environment that this and previous generations have created, particularly this generation, has caused and is causing
significant gestational and infant birth defects, aberrant
growth and development and subsequent disease. It is the
parents' responsibility for the diet of the infants and children
that leads to diabetes, obesity, cardiovascular disease, learning delay, and aberrant behavior. It is the parents' responsibility for the use/allowance of genetically engineered "foods" in
the diet; the widespread use of teratogenic, genotoxic, and
endocrine-disrupting chemicals and pesticides in the food and
environment, all causing infant and childhood disease. Children eat what their parents provide and model. More specifics
on these issues will be given later.

Since nutrition is the foundation/building block of our genes,
our cells, our tissues, our bodies, and all the microorganisms
that inhabit our bodies and everything around us in our environment, we must take a moment to look critically at the nu-

trition in the food. Consider the following chart of elements and the enzymes they activate. Though this is an abbreviated list, it shows that minerals are vital to every function of the human body. Every function of every cell, from protein production to detoxification, from oxygen utilization to hormone modulation, requires specific nutrients in order to occur. Keeping in mind the procession from health through pre-disease to disease to death, nutrient adequacy follows this same procession. In fact, it is truly the nutritional decline that is this procession and the states of being we call health, pre-disease, disease, and death are merely the outward manifestation of this inner elemental and molecular occurrence.

Metallo-Enzymes

Metal	Type of Enzyme	Role
Magnesium	Kinases, phosphatases, phosphodiesterases	Binding of phosphates and polyphosphates
Zinc	Metalloproteases, Dehydrogenases	Lewis acid carbonyl activation
Iron	Oxygenases (P450 Non-haem) [FeS] clusters	Binding and activation of oxygen Electron transport Hydratases
Copper	Oxygenases	Activation of oxygen
Manganese	Hydrolases, Hydratases	Lewis acid?
Cobalt	Vitamin B_{12} Coenzyme	Homolysis of Co-carbon bond
Molybdenum	Nitrogenase	Component of Mo/Fe Cluster
Calcium, phosphorous, selenium	Multiple	Multiple

Most people, including and partly because of doctors, take for granted that the food they eat provides all the necessary nutrition for them to maintain health. Notoriously, doctors tell their patients to simply eat a balanced diet and they will be fine. Everything that happens regarding their health is either genetics or happenstance (luck of the draw) in the doctors' minds. They go on to tell patients that taking nutritional supplements results in expensive urine. Then, of course, the same logic must hold true for all drugs the doctor prescribes because the majority of drugs are eventually excreted through the kidneys. So all that $150 cardiac medication, $114 acid blocker, the $100 cholesterol drug, and the $70 antidepressant all totaling $434 per month, results merely in expensive urine, too?

How does the doctor justify prescribing this "cheap" urine smorgasbord of drugs? The answer is that the drug alters body chemistry and physiology, and in the process of precipitating this change, the drug itself is altered, metabolized, and eventually excreted in the urine to be dumped from the body in its "used" form. This is exactly what happens with supplemental nutrients: they are taken into the body in one form or the other, some better, more biologically usable than others; do their job in altering body chemistry and physiology; and, in the process, are altered themselves, metabolized, and dumped from the body via the urine.

For example, antioxidants taken into the body in the chemically reduced form, such as reduced glutathione and reduced vitamin C, scavenge free radicals (electrical sparks in the system) so these "sparks" don't damage our cells. In the process of scavenging these "electrical sparks" the antioxidant becomes "oxidized" rendering it useless as an antioxidant. The body either recycles the "oxidized antioxidant," such as is the case of glutathione, or it must eliminate it from the body, such as is the case with vitamin C, which it readily does via the urine.

Take calcium as another example. We dump about 1000mg of calcium daily from our body via normal metabolism, especially bone osteoclast activity. We must replace that 1000mg on average, daily, to replenish normal metabolism, especially bone osteoblast activity. The main difference between drugs and nutrients is that drugs, to do what they do in the body, changing body chemistry and metabolism—hopefully for the better, which is why your doctor prescribed the medication— actually require nutrients for them to work and, consequently, deplete the body of various nutrients differing from drug to drug. Examples of nutrients depleted by drugs include: Acid blockers deplete vitamins B_{12} and D, calcium, iron, zinc, and folate. Aspirin depletes vitamins C and B_5, calcium, folate, iron, potassium, and sodium, Statins deplete CoQ10. Corticosteroids deplete calcium, chromium, potassium, selenium, and vitamins B_6, B_{12}, and D.

Subsequently, in the standard medical model of practice, the patient's body is continuously and systematically depleted of nutrition both through negligence in repletion food and in depletion by medical therapy. Over time, the patient is guaranteed to slip from the pre-disease state into the disease state and, finally, agonizing death. It's the business of disease, pure and simple. The modern model places all the profitability on the disease state. The treatment itself leads to further disease eliciting additional nutrient depleting treatment which leads, yet again, to additional disease and yet more nutrient depleting treatment *ad nauseum* until death of the patient.

Where is the nutrition? Look at the diet of today, the SAD plan, the Standard American Diet. "Fast food" is the norm. The majority of households no longer cook and dine at home.

Most of what they do eat at home is prepared elsewhere and brought back to the home for consumption. Much of the food is processed, further reducing the already depleted level of nutrition. The result is a plethora of "hollow calories" giving people full stomachs though they starve to death for lack of nutrition as evidenced by the burgeoning obesity and diabetes statistics.

Why should we eat at all? The doctors say that supplementation just makes for expensive urine. By that logic we should stop eating and drinking anything because most of the water and beverage we drink is just urinated out and the majority of all the food we eat goes out the other end as fecal matter. Just think of how much we could save in environmental costs if we just stopped producing all that unnecessary urine and fecal matter. The only things we would really need are those "inexpensive" drugs. But of course with "free healthcare for all" these drugs are "inexpensive." After all, how much cheaper can they get than "free"?

What about the people who really pay attention to what they eat, frequent the farmers' markets, the organic foods stores, the "health food" stores, the CSAs (community supported agriculture, food subscription membership farms), or their own gardens? Aren't these people getting nutritious foods, yet they are still sick? This is sad but true for the most part. The problem rests in the nutrient value of the foods themselves, not from a genetics perspective, rather from a farm/garden management perspective.

Take a mixed green and vegetable salad: several different lettuces, spinach, kale, cucumber, onion, olives, sweet peppers, avocado, tomato, radish, carrot, and chopped celery. Looks good, the veggies are "fresh" and it is topped with olive oil and vinaigrette dressing. It should be a nourishing meal, but is it? If we analyze the nutrient level or density of this salad and compare the results to the results of the same salad mix from 1940, we would find that this wonderful looking fresh salad is between 16 and 76 percent lower in nutrients (meaning vitamins and minerals) today.

In other words, the level of calcium, potassium, iron, zinc, folic acid, and vitamin C are significantly less today than they would have been in 1940. But wait a minute, we have made great strides in agriculture and food production since 1940. We feed the world. Yes, we have new hybrid vegetable varieties; yes, we have higher analysis fertilizers and apply much more of them today; yes, we have precision farming equipment fitted with global GPS guidance systems; yes, we have more toxic and lethal pesticides—we have an unending list of things today we didn't have in 1940.

Most importantly, today we have less nutrition per pound of food product consumed. Today we have much more hollow calories, significantly deficient in basic minerals and vitamins. Today we have more crop diseases and insect damage. According to the U.S. Geological Survey in 1991, even though pesticide use has increased over thirteen times, crop loss due to insect pests has doubled. Today we have more pollution of our food, water, soil, and people. Today we have innumerable drug and chemical resistant diseases, weeds and insect pests. Today we have a logarithmic increase in birth defects, learning disabilities and behavioral problems in children, infertility, miscarriages, early life cancers, diabetes and obesity not seen anywhere close to this rate in 1940. Today we have more hunger and poverty today than we did in 1940.[1]

It is amazing how many people will state that things are just fine with our food and technology because we have a longer life expectancy today than ever before. What they fail to understand or deliberately neglect is that the increase in "average" life expectancy is tied to improvements in public health and hygiene, not to medicine or agriculture. These pundits also neglect to acknowledge that today's generation is expected to have a shorter life expectancy than their parents; so much for the benefit of technology and medicine.

If we look at life expectancy from birth to death, yes, our average expectancy has improved; however, when we look at life expectancy from age 65 to death, we have only improved by three to four years from 1900 to 2000. Our country's founding fathers, the fifty-six delegates who signed the Declaration of Independence, lived to an average age of 67. John Adams lived to 90 and Johnson to 92. A few, Franklin, Madison, Williamson, and Wythe, lived into their 80s. Remember, this was over 200 years ago. There were no indoor toilets, no modern conveniences we take for granted today, such as central heating and cooling.[2]

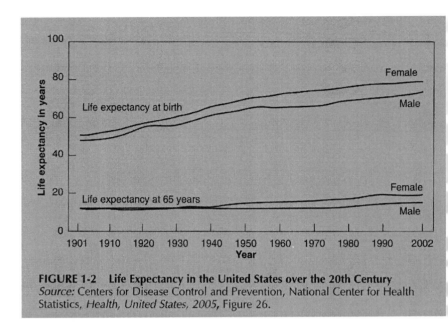

FIGURE 1-2   Life Expectancy in the United States over the 20th Century
Source: Centers for Disease Control and Prevention, National Center for Health Statistics, *Health, United States, 2005,* Figure 26.

People want to believe that technology, just for the sake of technology, is always good and always advances our quality of life on planet earth. That is simply not true. If the technology eventually kills the experimenter, it is not good technology, and that is exactly the case with current agricultural biotechnology as well as the "green revolution" for the most part. Technology is just a tool as Abraham, et al., put it.[3]

A graph from *Mother Earth News*, October/November 2008, of USDA data, shows how modern agricultural technology has changed our food. Farmers do, in fact, produce more calories today per acre than in times past. The problem is that these calories are "hollow" calories; calories without adequate vitamin and mineral nutrition. Diabetes and obesity are the natural consequence of such food production. The data shows that Americans consumed over 2,750 calories in 2000 compared to just over 2,250 calories in 1970. American's consumed nearly 200 pounds per person of refined grains in 2000 compared to less than 140 pounds in 1970 and 155 pounds in 1950. Americans consumed about 150 pounds per person of refined sweetener in 2000 compared to about 110 in 1950.

Analysis of crops and the findings of nutrient decline did not start recently. They are repeated themes. Steiner talked about nutrient decline in the 1920s. Charles Northern read into the Congressional Record in 1936 that gastrointestinal diseases were correlated with nutrient decline in the food. The following excerpt is yet another display of modern agriculture's blatant failure to produce health-sustaining food:

> "Spectrometer analyses of over 4,000 grain samples taken in 11 Midwest states over just the last 4 years indicate an unmistakable decline in trace minerals. . . . The average copper content in all

the corn analyses . . . 2.56 ppm . . . but for the
last year 1968 was less than 0.82 ppm . . . a drop
of approximately 70 percent. The hog man may
notice that his animals are quite nervous . . .
magnified if the animal is put under any stress . .
. animals being loaded into a truck for market
began to shake and quiver and had trouble stand-
ing." *National Hog Farmer*, Swine Information
Service, No. E25, 1968.

When one realizes that food is medicine, it is sustenance, it is

the very ingredient necessary for the body to be healthy, vi-

able, and productive, the picture becomes clearer that all this

"wonderful" agricultural production technology lavished by

the biotech media has done little to address world hunger;

rather, it has depleted both our food supply of nutrition and

our environment of its life force. How can one possibly con-

tend that our technology and food production industry has

progressed, has advanced, when considering that mixed salad

mentioned previously is LESS of a food/nutrient source than

it was in 1940? After all, food is supposed to be first and

foremost, THE supply of nutrition for our bodies!

If one has a high-performance car whose engine requires

premium-grade gasoline to run efficiently and smoothly, can

he contend that simply giving it MORE regular grade gasoline makes it run just fine? Can he contend that, because he can produce and supply more regular-grade gasoline for this premium-grade car, he has done well, he should be praised, he should be rewarded to continue producing this sub-grade gasoline because he has perfected the efficient manufacturing of such a product? NO!

The reality is, who cares if you have perfected the production of this sub-grade gasoline, my car needs premium-grade gasoline and no quantity in the world of regular, sub-grade gasoline will suffice! Ladies and gentlemen, this is the state of our food chain. Humans and animals require premium-grade food for their bodies to "run properly" and what we have is a glut of sub-grade food produced worldwide. People want to equate quantity with quality because modern agriculture is so prolific with the quantity, yet fails to supply the quality of food we need to truly be healthy. This quantity mindset permeates doctors and dieticians alike.

Dieticians are trained and entranced with the concept of fat, protein, and carbohydrate. Little or no attention is given to neither the source nor the characteristic of the fat, protein, or carbohydrate. The first big push, continued to this day, is the insistence of "low fat" everything, especially low saturated fats; consequently, the public has been hoodwinked into believing that fat in the diet equates to fat around the belly and increased incidence of various cancers such as colon and breast cancers. A study published in 1996 comparing Mediterranean women to American women and their respective breast cancer rates found that women in the Mediterranean consumed nearly twice the fat per day in their diet as did American women, yet their breast cancer rates were significantly lower than those of American women.

The key was the quality of the fat, not the quantity of the fat. American women consumed vegetable and trans-fats while the Mediterranean women consumed mono- and polyunsaturated fat—olive oil. The work done by Westin A. Price, and now taught by Sally Fallon, shows that our bodies need healthful, unprocessed fats to function properly. The "ketogenic diet" developed decades ago for children with developmental disorders, proved that what was missing in these children's diet necessary for brain development was appropriate FAT.

The point is that fat or carbohydrate or protein, per se, is neither the issue nor that simple. It is the quality of each of these, in balance, plus the overall nutrient density—amount of vitamins, minerals, amino acids, antioxidants and fatty acids— that counts. A candy bar with nuts provides fat, protein, and carbohydrate, which is fine for maintaining blood glucose levels and satiation temporarily, but little in the way of nutrition for the body to fend off infections, detoxify, replicate cells, rebuild tissue, and maintain bone density. The same goes for this salad mentioned earlier. It is more and more like "filler" than food; actually, more like "poisoned filler" than food, considering all the pesticide residue "food" now carries.

The same holds for data from abroad. An analysis of The Composition of Foods, Ministry of Agriculture, Fisheries and Foods and the Royal Society of Chemistry, UK, as was done by David Thomas.[4] He compared the nutrient analysis of foods between 1940 and 1991, which showed significant nutrient decline in the food. Why would we expect anything different? The Brits have adopted and developed the same nutrient depleting "American Green Revolution" technology as has the U.S.

This is a precarious topic, agricultural technology, farm management, crop production. Most of the consuming public is not real interested because it is so disconnected from the farm, the greenhouse, the vineyard, the orchard, the garden; yet, the consuming public has the real and ultimate power to change how its food is produced. Every day the consumer votes with his/her money spent at the store. That vote determines what will be on the shelf tomorrow or next week or next month/year.

The consumer needs to understand just a few fundamental facts about the food he or she purchases at the store. Taste and aesthetics are the two most important purchasing incentives for the consumer. Fact: The better the nutrient density/content of ANY fruit, vegetable, nut, or seed, the better it will taste and the better it will look, the longer it will store in the refrigerator without rotting. Much of the produce consumers buy today turns to slimy mush in the refrigerator after just a few days. Leave an apple or peach out on the counter and it soon is covered with fuzz and turns to a slimy, disgusting pile of mush, attracting flies and ants. Most children and adults don't like many vegetables because they taste terrible. Celery is bitter, stringy, and hollow. Broccoli is bitter and tastes like cardboard. Peaches are bland, pithy, and tasteless. Strawberries are hollow, sour to bitter, and must be coated with sugar to tolerate. Taste is about nutrient profile. Raw foods taste terrible because they have such a poor nutritional profile—that's farm management failure—not genetics, not imagination, not anything other than neglectful farm management.

More on this later when I discuss farm management and how we solve this problem. Know for now that science proves food is less nutritious today and continues to decline in nutrient density with "modern farming" practice. Most importantly, we have the technology to completely reverse this trend while simultaneously cleaning up the environment, sequestering greenhouse gasses, and feeding the world.

---

1   2013 World Hunger and Poverty Facts and Statistics World Hunger Education Service.
http://www.worldhunger.org/articles/Learn/world%20hunger%20fact s%202002.htm[2]America's Founding Fathers: Delegates to the Constitutional Convention. The Charters of Freedom.

2   http://www.archives.gov/exhibits/charters/constitution_founding_ fathers_overview.html

3   Hobbelink H, Vellve R, Abraham M. "Inside the biorevolution: a citizens action resource guide on biotechnology and third world agriculture." Penang: International Organization of Consumers Union; Barcelona Genetic Resources Action International; 1990.

4   Analysis of UK Composition of Foods 1940–1991. Nutrition and Health 2003, Vol.17, pp. 85-115 from The Composition of Foods, Ministry of Agriculture, Fisheries and Foods and the Royal Society of Chemistry.

Chapter 3
Genetic Engineering

One can never solve a problem by applying the same logic that was used in creating the problem in the first place.

—Albert Einstein.

This proverb applies as much today as ever before. The logic of chemical agriculture is that insect pests, diseases, and weeds are all due to pesticide (chemical weapons) deficiencies and, thus, solved by more applications of stronger chemical weapons. These applications further deplete the nutritional and biological balance in the soil and crops, which makes them yet more susceptible to predators—insect pests, diseases, and weeds. It is the perfect logic to perpetuate the chemical weapons industry started during World War I and greatly expanded during World War II.

The logic employed by the biotechnology industry for the genetic engineering of crops extends this "chemical weapons deficiency" working model to the laboratory. The genetic engineer seeks to produce these chemical weapons inherently within the crop itself and/or synthetically manipulate the crop metabolism so that more chosen chemicals (RoundUp, 2,4-D, Basta are the front runners), herbicides in these cases, can be applied to the crop. These chemicals further deplete the soil and plant health precipitating yet more insect pests, disease and weeds. Genetic engineering of crops is a designed expansion and perpetuation of the chemical weapons treadmill. The more chemicals used, the more that can be and are "needed" to be used. It is a brilliant business plan for the chemical weapons industry. The very use of their products create an environment where yet more chemical use if "justified" guaranteeing the sale of more and more chemical weapons. Unfortunately, this mentality and greed also assures further pollution of the environment, expanded animal and human disease and suffering.

The fundamental logic employed by this industry, the university professors that perpetuate the belief that Nature is flawed, man's enemy, and must be subdued with more powerful chimerical weapons and/or "corrected" or "circumvented" with genetic engineering technology.

Society in general respects the engineer as he or she has done so much to improve our lifestyle, reduce our labors, and improve our efficiencies. It seemed a natural step to entrust engineers to "correct the flaws of Nature" when it came to living organisms. After all, man is so much better equipped to understand how organisms need to function for the sustainment of human civilization, right? Of course, we need food to feed the ever-expanding world population. Nature just doesn't understand that moral quest, that humanitarian calling. How sad so many people actually believe that fiction.

Most importantly, that fictional concept of life on planet Earth promised patentable assets, which meant cash flow, royalties, research grants, headlines in the news, pats on the back; it meant possible monopoly, perhaps complete monopolization of the entire agricultural industry, the largest, surest industry in the world. As Presidents Roosevelt, Nixon, and Obama were/are good at doing, tell the public a lie often enough and eventually the public will believe it as truth; and, so has a great number of people believed the fiction that genetically engineered foods are the savior of humankind—safe, and essentially the same as any other food.

Keep in mind the fact that insect and disease pressure/invasion of a crop are purely correlated to nutritional mismanagement by the farmer. They are not due to pesticide deficiencies; they are not due to genetic screw-ups by nature. Consequently, the purported correction of or treatment for insect and disease infestation of crops via genetic engineering is pure nonsense. One cannot correct an error that does not exist. Such a "quest" can create and has created an error that did not previously exist.

Consider the track that has led to genetically engineered crops. World War I began the commercial use of chemical weapons of war and World War II greatly expanded the production of nitrates for bomb making. After World War II, the chemical weapons and bomb-making industries were seeking ways to continue their very profitable and expansive businesses. Agriculture was the logical gift child of these industries as the British government had mandated the use of nitrogen fertilizers during World War II in the name of providing food for the war effort.

It became clear that such fertilization led to more insect and disease pressure providing an ever-expanding demand for chemical weapons, subsequently called pesticides (the term chemical weapons is not politically correct) and subsequently today called "plant protection products," which is much more politically correct than pesticides in our age of political correctness. As this agricultural management program perpetuated around the industrialized world, food produced under said management consistently declined in nutritional value. As the crops declined in nutritional value/density, they became sicker and more susceptible to diseases and insect pests.

Additionally, due to the narrower and narrower nutrient spectrum of said fertilizer programs, native and open pollinated varieties of foods that had sustained humans for thousands of years were unable to grow well under such deficient conditions. These varieties were quickly replaced by "new and improved" hybrids selected for their ability to grow volume under deprived nutrient conditions. But these new hybrid varieties were very susceptible to disease and insect pests so, yet more chemical weapons had to be used. It was a brilliant business plan.

Over time, yet more "new and improved" hybrid varieties had to be developed, "new and improved" chemical weapons had to be developed to combat the ever-increasing resistant diseases and insect pests along with resistant weeds. With the advent of genetic engineering technology, companies saw ways to further monopolize on seed varieties, actually obtain patents for seeds, which allowed for further marketing of their in-house chemical weapons.

The first genetically engineered commercialized crops were for tolerance to the herbicide RoundUp. This made it possible for farmers to spray this broad-spectrum herbicide on corn and soybeans, normally "killed" from RoundUp application. Farmers saw this as very convenient and bought the "Emperor's new clothing" without question. The manufacturer, Monsanto, funded university research heavily and convinced politicians that biotechnology was the way of the future. Few people stopped to ask whether this technology was, first, needed, and, second, safe. There was too much money to be made to ask such inconvenient questions. The answer to both questions is a resounding NO, NEVER, NADA!

Unfortunately, politicians, university researchers, and industry salespeople are so drunk with cash flow that they cannot envision life without such drunkenness and producers have so far drank the company Kool-Aid that they can't imagine farming without it. As a result, we have an explosion of resistant diseases, insect pests, weeds, and human and animal illnesses that can be linked directly back to this failed system. Ultimately, however, the consumer holds the real power and as consumers vote daily with their dollars in favor of non-GMO foods, the "Emperor's new clothing" will soon pass into oblivion where it belongs.

Below is a listing of the touted benefits of genetically engineered crops and the actual results that have come about over the past thirty years.

Touted Benefits	Actual Results
Higher yields	lower
More nutrition	less
Fewer pesticides	more
Less post-harvest loss	more
Improve N-fixation	less
Drought and salt tolerance	less
Increased photosynthesis	less
Greater root growth & function	less
Disease resistance	less
Lower risks (economic)	more
Lower costs	more
Greater safety	less
Simpler management	resistant weeds & pests

Ultimately, genetic engineering of foods is an exercise in the betrayal of public trust.[1]

Selling this fiction to the public, to the farmer (the easiest sell), required enlisting Hollywood and a long list of "promises." The chemical weapons industry is flush with cash, so Hollywood's part was easy as filmmakers, advertising firms, and media will say anything for a buck.

The issues that may seem appealing to the consumer or what Hollywood has portrayed that genetically engineered foods (GMOs) bring to the table have been the promises to bring technology to bear on the problem of world hunger; the problem of the ever-increasing world population; the problem of pesky insects stealing our valued food supplies; the growing of food crops in the midst of drought and especially countering the crisis of man-made global warming; the nutritional enhancement of food staples such as rice to address the public health crises in the developing world of vitamin A deficiency causing blindness; the reduction in the use of chemical weapons on our food crops.

Who could possibly be against such benevolent and humanitarian, not to mention environmentally responsible, technology? My goodness, one would have to be mean spirited and anti-human to be against such wonderful technology wouldn't he? It's that utopian society promise again espoused by Lenin, Marx, Stalin, FDR, Hitler, Mau, Reagan, Clinton, and Obama. That is, of course, if the purported claims were actually true, which they are NOT!

The biotech industry has spent hundreds of millions of dollars in ad campaigns to make the discussion regarding the acceptance and use of genetically engineered crops a political, and most importantly, a philosophical and social/moral debate, keeping, at all cost, the discussion out of the scientific, particularly the medical science arena. They, the biotech industry, know they cannot win a scientific debate because none, I said NONE, of their platform stands up to scientific scrutiny. I realize that this is a pretty contentious statement for how could all these university researchers, government bureaucracies (USDA, FDA) and private companies be so onboard with genetically engineered crops if there weren't at least some science backing it up? Simple answer: Follow the money.

First, as already mentioned, NONE of the promises for better yield, better nutrition, lower pesticide use, etc., have materialized after twenty-five years of imposed genetically engineered crops. Quite the contrary. We now have more insect and disease problems in both crops and consumers, we have better yields in non-genetically engineered crops than genetically engineered crops, we have much increased use of pesticides, especially glyphosate, per acre per crop than ever before in history. Consequently, we have more environmental and human assault (birth defects, miscarriages, endocrine diseases, and cancer, especially in children) than ever before. We now have contaminated much of the world food supply, many native plants, and the microbial populations in the digestive systems of most people with foreign, gene disrupting genetic material triggering inherent inflammation in every human and animal.

A priori, we have precipitated a biomolecular infective molecule correlated to genetically engineered crops and glyphosate application. This agent, being a biomolecular matrix, is not living; therefore, is not responsive to any antibiotics, antivirals, antiparasitics, or antifungals. It is associated with infertility and spontaneous abortion in animals and humans.

How is it possible for any of these above-named problems to be true, and yet, genetically engineered crops have been approved by USDA and FDA for planting and consumption? The simple answer: Follow the money. At the end of this section you will find the long list of scientific references substantiating every statement and assertion I have made. Many of these citations are from scientists doing their research under the aegis of the USDA, as well as at notable American and international universities, both in agriculture and medicine. Unfortunately, many of these scientists, upon releasing their findings, are threatened with defunding, with ridicule, with character assassination, and even firing because, via their intellectual honesty, they reported truthful evidence contrary to the party line.

Second, as already covered previously in the discussion about food quality, the presence of insect pests and disease organisms is NOT a genetic defect or fault; rather, their presence is precipitated by poor nutritional management. Again, these are not from genetic faults. They are not from a deficiency of man-made genetic engineering interventions. This is perhaps one of the most difficult concepts, if not the most difficult concept, for the average person to grasp: thinking, understanding, realizing that insect pests and disease organisms are expected and appropriate consequences of plant nutritional crisis. Full and complete nutrition is needed for a plant to take raw materials, minerals, carbon dioxide, water, and nitrogen and manufacture flawless plant material. Insects do NOT attack healthy plants. They only attack sick plants. That is their job, to recycle food crops not sufficiently mineralized to supply mammals with health-sustaining nutrition.

This process begins with free nitrogen compounds of ammonia and nitrate, converting them to a full complement of amino acids in a required ratio of each to all the others, eventually combining these amino acids into peptides, large proteins, glycoproteins, and enzymes to replicate cells, grow tissue, and mature crops. If, at any time along the "assembly line" in this manufacturing process, there is a deficiency of nutrients, the "line" gets backed up and free nitrogen compounds spill over. THESE are the readily "insect digestible" foods that attract insects to the table as well as disease organisms. Think of what would happen on an assembly line manufacturing cars if inventory ran out of doors, steering wheels, shift levers, and taillights. The assembly line will get jammed up with all these half-built cars, viable but not drivable.

Because the assembly line is backed up, the plant's needed final products are reduced, its immunity is compromised, which further allows disease organisms to take advantage of the spilled over free nitrogen compounds. This is the classical garbage and rat infestation issue. What came first, the rats or the garbage? Are the rats there bringing in the garbage or is the garbage providing the food attractant for the rats? Clean up the garbage, the simple resolution, and the rats leave or starve to death.

The digestive systems of insect pests are not geared to digest complete, healthy plant material, which is why, when plants are truly healthy, they are not bothered by insect pests and pathogens. This is part of the recycling process of nature to maintain survival of the fittest. If insects were random, ravenous consumers as the chemical industry would like the public to believe, plant life would never have survived all the thousands or millions of years. Insects and disease organisms are truly our quality control workers.

There is an interesting article titled "Organically Grown Food Provides Health Benefits to Drosophilia melanogaster." Chhabra R, Kolli S, Bauer JH (2013) Organically Grown Food Provides Health Benefits to Drosophila melanogaster. PLoS ONE 8(1): e52988. doi:10.1371/journal.pone. This article is about a science project done by a middle school student, Ria Chhabra from Texas. She wanted to see if organic foods were better than not organic foods. She chose fruit flies because they are a common choice "animal" for scientific studies. She found that fruit flies fed organic fruits had better fertility and longer life than those fruit flies fed conventional fruits.

That is a nice finding except for a very important fact. Fruit flies are only attracted to fruits that are nutritionally deficient as mentioned before; so even though the organic fruits were shown to be higher than the conventional in vitamins and key nutrients, the organic fruits were still a long way from being of the quality they can and should be. The work done by Dr. Tom Dykstra of Dykstra Labs in Gainesville, Florida, shows that nutrition does affect fertility and longevity of insects and sick insects will be infected with viruses and parasites just as any other sick organism. The key to understand is that if the organic fruits in this study had been truly nutrient dense and high brix, the fruit flies would not have eaten them at all.

Unfortunately, farming technology today is so inept at soil and plant nutrition, it is rare to find food crops that are truly healthy, having an excellent brix (discussed later) reading. People have grown to accept "mediocre" as the norm. This applies to both "organically grown" and "conventionally grown" foods and will as long as the farmer follows standard soil testing protocols and recommendations. These protocols and recommendations are designed to maintain the status quo, which guarantees plenty of "garbage" to attract the "sanitation crew" that perpetuates the sale of chemical weapons.

What the consumer needs to understand is that all the insect problems complained about and experienced by farmers, greenhouse growers and gardeners are largely self-induced. Nutritional mismanagement is the culprit, not an "insecticide deficiency." Nature is not out to "get the farmer." Insect problems are solved by the consumer demanding better quality food forcing the grower to learn appropriate nutritional management or get out of the business.

A significant percentage of pesticides used today are accounted for by herbicides (weed killers) and the most common genetically engineered crop trait is for herbicide resistance. This means that the farmer can spray herbicide, glyphosate being the most common, directly on the growing crop without killing the crop, outright. This practice is desirous so the farmer can target weeds in the crop with a universal herbicide. It's a great theory and resulted in glyphosate being the first billion-dollar herbicide.

The problem is that glyphosate resistant weeds now abound around the world precipitating increased use of additional herbicides. Glyphosate has been proven to be extremely toxic to the environment, animals, and people. It has been found to cause birth defects and cancer, remains in the environment for decades (half-life possibly over twenty-two years), is associated with reduced nutrient metabolism in the crop, kills beneficial microorganisms, and leads to increased proliferation of pathogenic microorganisms including fusarium and *C. botulinium* precipitating increased use of insecticides and fungicides.

Weeds are associated with soil fertility mismanagement. Improved soil management reduces broadleaf weeds by over 75 percent according to USDA Soil Tilth Lab research. Grass weeds are addressed by appropriate soil calcium nutrition. A great majority of farmers rely on USDA Cooperative Extension Service information for soil testing, recommendations, and fertility management. The agents follow the party line, which perpetuates the sale of more chemical weapons. Soil nutritional management does not sell a lot of chemical so it does not get any significant press or academic support. Consequently, farmers hear little if any instruction about soil management and nutrition for addressing weeds, diseases, and insects.

Summarizing where we are in this discussion, nutrition is the key to health and the imbalance and deficiency of nutrition are the key to pre-disease and disease. Nutritional management requires thought, study, and execution of a management plan. Much simpler and less intellectually challenging is the following of procedural protocols dictated by chemical weapons manufacturers' sales recommendations. The farmer need only purchase the chemical and get it applied on a timely basis prescribed by the manufacturer. If more is needed, that solution is also scripted. If the process fails, more poison is recommended, and when that doesn't work, the weather, the genetics, the "environmentalists," the government, or someone or something else is blamed for the failure. Insurance is usually mandated by the banking system so there is little consequence to the farmer, the University Extension Service, and chemical company for following the status quo. The bill is picked up by the taxpayer.

As this system has gotten more dilapidated and disease ridden, insect and weed infested, the "logical" culprit is Nature. The solution certainly must be the human engineering of the genetics of the plants so that human interventions can be ramped up further to kill Nature's flawed responses. After all, it is war, man against Nature, and by dollar we are going to wage this war, ad infinitum. The "war machine" is designed to be perpetual, self-justifying, and, of course, "necessary."

The point that the reader must get is that the war is not necessary, not even remotely successful as the collateral damage far out costs the proposed gains. Nutrient value of food has declined and continues to decline. Weeds, diseases, and insect pests cause more economic loss today than fifty years ago. We have more *E. coli*, salmonella and MRSA risk in and on food today than ever before. Most importantly, all these issues are successfully addressed and corrected by appropriate nutritional farm management. The collateral effect of appropriate management regenerates the environment and the consumer, restores solvency to the family farm and presents the opportunity for consumers to be healthy if they choose.

Genetic engineering of crops is another excuse to continue dirty, nutritionally deficient, toxic, prescription farm management. It is not at all like natural plant or animal breeding. It is akin to viral infection; actually, it IS viral infection. The process requires isolating a gene codon, attaching it to a carrier, today agrobacterium or clavibacter as the vector, adding a virus to activate the codon, and attaching an antibiotic resistance gene as a marker for the desired codon.

This complex is "thrown" into the plant cell, soy, corn, beet, etc. A small percentage of cells will become infected with the engineered gene codon. These cells are grown out in cell culture into plants, cloned and grown out further and eventually seed is produced with this artificially infected, engineered trait.

Because genetic engineering is NOT in any way like natural plant breeding, genetically engineered plant material is foreign to all mammalian digestive systems. It is recognized by the immune system as "foreign" and triggers an inflammatory response, 100 percent of the time. The most universal consequence seen in all animal studies is digestive system inflammation, cellular hypertrophy, and pathology.

Considering nothing else, one must ask how in the world could anyone suggest that genetically engineered (GE) "foods" could be essentially the same as normal foods, non-genetically engineered foods, when every study shows inflammatory response and cellular change due to genetically engineered food being fed? If the immune system responds negatively to one "food" and not to another, supposedly equivalent, the two are NOT equivalent. That is basic immunology.

A superb review article on genetically engineered crops and glyphosate was done by N. L. Swanson. She gathered the statistics from government sources and plotted the graphs overlying the use trends of GMO crops and glyphosate with incidence trends for various cancers, obesity, diabetes and blood pressure, birth defects and child behavior diagnoses, dementia and Alzheimer's incidences, and finally gastrointestinal disorders. It is a must-read for consumers and professionals alike.[2]

---

1   Huber, PhD, Don. Public Presentation, Riverside, Iowa. December, 2012.

2   Genetically Modified Organisms and the deterioration of health in the United States. N. L. Swanson, 4/24/2013. This document was first published as a series of articles on Seattle examiner.com

Chapter 4

Genetic Roulette: Science Proves GMOs To Be Toxic

The problem with genetic roulette is that all six chambers of the revolver are loaded, unlike Russian roulette where only one chamber is loaded. Willful ignorance is defined by Eben Alexander, M.D., in his book *Proof of Heaven,* as the belief that one knows the truth without needing to look at the facts. In other words, the biotech industry, its academic call-men and mindless investors are of the mindset of "don't confuse us with the facts because we have already made up our minds." I prefer to look at the facts and the facts prove genetically engineered "foods" to be toxic, inflammatory, carcinogenic, and nutritionally deplete. Most ridiculous is the fact that they are not "needed", fulfill no biological deficit, have no scientific foundation, and accelerate environmental pollution.

There is an excellent video titled, "Genetic Roulette" http://geneticroulettemovie.com/. I highly recommend watching it. It is a reasonable summary about genetically engineered crops and the biotech industry in general. In this chapter, I will expand on the research that has been done on genetically engineered crops starting with animal studies.

The first GE tomato was the FlavrSavr. Rats in the feeding studies failed to eat it on their own. (This is a common observation. Wild and domesticated animals when given a choice between genetically engineered crops v. non-genetically engineered crops, 100 percent of the times choose the non-GE crop. Only when they are force-fed, have no choice and are hungry will they consume genetically engineered crops.) When force-fed the GE tomato, after twenty-eight days, seven of twenty rats developed stomach lesions; another seven died within two weeks.

Rat studies with GE potatoes showed potentially pre-cancerous cell growth in the digestive system, had smaller brains, smaller livers, and smaller testicles and immune changes (*Lancet* 1999). Monsanto's own studies on rats fed GE corn showed indicators for liver and kidney toxicity, blood pressure dysregulation, allergies, blood sugar elevation, and anemia. Again, if the GE crop is "essentially the same" as the non-GE crop, how could there possibly be these differences in the animal responses to consuming it?

Chickens fed GE corn died at twice the rate. Mice fed GE soy showed reduced pancreatic enzymes, altered pancreatic cell structure, and altered gene expression. Their livers showed cell damage, altered gene expression and elevated enzymes. Their testicles showed altered structure and function.

A very telling study using GE soy on pregnant rats carried out by Ermakova at the Russian Academy of Science. Her study showed a significant increase in death rate of pups, retarded growth of pups, and infertility of the second generation in the GE soy-fed test animals.

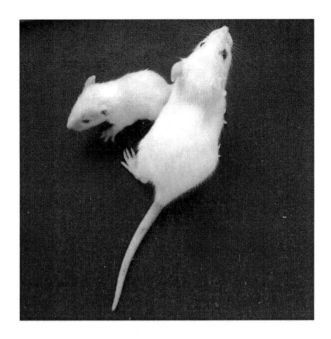

Nineteen-day-old rats. Larger rat is from control group; smaller from GM-soy-fed group.

Also at the Russian Academy of Science, using hamsters, Surov found complete infertility by the third generation of GE soy-fed animals. Another concerning aberration seen in the GMO soy-fed hamsters was the manifestation of pouches of hair growth in the hamster's mouths.[1]

A mice study done by the Veterinary University Vienna, Austrian Agency for Health and Food Safety, Austrian Federal

Ministry of Health, Family, and Youth, showed similar findings of infertility along with decreased litter and pup size in the third and fourth generations fed GE food.[2]

Unfortunately, there are a number of political hacks whose sole purpose is to discredit ANY research that shows problems with genetically engineered crops.

"1.14—Ermakova's findings defy logic," Academic Reviews http://academicsreview.org/reviewed-content/genetic-roulette/section-1/1-14-roundup-ready-soy-is-safe-5/

Academic Reviews is a tax free 501C3 entity that claims to exist to " . . . ensure that sound science is widely and easily available to inform us . . . " http://academicsreview.org/about-academic-review/purpose/ One of the co-founders of this organization is Bruce Chassy, who has a long list of appointments on Illinois university and government committees to suggest his qualification as a scientist to co-found Academic Reviews. Too bad he is just another politician paid for by the industry. "Bruce Chassy presents himself as a public-sector scientist, but he has received multiple research grants from biotech companies."

http://scienceblogs.com/tomorrowstable/2012/10/18/letter-to-dr-oz-show-producers-by-bruce-chassy-phd-academics-review/

It is a repeating theme: Just follow the money. Every pundit of genetically engineered crops is tied directly or indirectly to the biotech industry–funding nipple. The industry is persistent. It flashes money around to the various universities whose department heads are then obliged to patronize biotechnology. Further, these pundits, including obliging university professors, routinely present themselves as independent scientists who legitimately understand all the issues of biotechnology and, thus, are fully qualified to discredit the likes of any and all scientists presenting research contrary to the party line.

Ermakova had two strikes against her in the eyes of people such as Chassy. She did her own research on genetically engineered soy with rats and she reviewed the 1998 Russian study on genetically engineered potatoes supported by Monsanto. Her review merely paraphrased the condemning evidence GMOs generated by the study, but that was not politically correct of her to do so. The Russian study wasn't released until 2005 after "the Nikulinski District Court in Russia ruled that information relating to the safety of GM food should be open to the public."[3]

Purdue University, Iowa State University, and many others, along with other industry mouthpieces, have repeatedly made statements to discredit Dr. Don Huber, Professor Emeritus, Purdue University. Dr. Huber spent twenty-five years as a lead research scientist at Purdue for Monsanto. He is intimately knowledgeable about RoundUp/glyphosate, the pesticide industry, and the inner workings and politics of both industry corporations and university associates. He is one of the most respected and sought-after plant nutrition and plant pathology experts in the world. His credentials are impeccable and his military service as a lead scientist tasked with identifying and warning the U.S. government about biological weapons threats is noteworthy.[4/5]

May 19, 2009 the American Academy of Environmental Medicine (AAEM) issued the following statement:

> "Avoid GM (genetically modified) foods when possible. . . . Several animal studies indicate serious health risks associated with GM food. . . .

> There is more than a casual association between
> GM foods and adverse health effects. There is cau-
> sation. . . . The strength of association and consis-
> tency between GM foods and disease is confirmed
> in several animal studies."

The first human study inadvertently occurred in 1987. It became known as the infamous L-tryptophan debaucher. L-
tryptophan is an amino acid precursor of serotonin and many
people were taking it for depressive symptoms. It seemed to
be a valuable and beneficial supplement. There were over
1,500 reported cases of EMS (eosinophilia-myalgia syndrome)
and 39 deaths. Every case was attributed to the Shera Dinko
L-tryptophan manufactured via genetically engineered bacteria. The notorious "contamination" of the L-tryptophan supply
purported by the FDA was solely the genetically engineered
manufactured product. There was no contamination of any
standard non-GMO manufactured product. There were no
cases of EMS from non-GMO L-tryptophan.

A big problem with the genetic engineering process is that it
results in unpredicted and toxic byproducts. This is the probable "contamination" found in L-tryptophan described above.

Analysis of the 2012 U.S. GMO corn crop has found very high levels of formaldehyde. No mechanism other than endogenous production of this serious carcinogen can be explained. It appears to be the consequent product of the aberrant genetic infection in the GMO corn. Note also the reduced mineral levels in the GMO corn compared to the non-GMO corn.

Nutrient Density of GMO & Non-GMO Corn, Iowa 2012					
Nutrient	GMO	Non-GMO	Nutrient	GMO	Non-GMO
Glyphosate	13	0	Mn	2	14
Formaldehyde	200	0	Fe	2	14
Test Wt.	57.5	61.5	Zn	2.3	14.3
Brix	1	20	Cu	2.6	16
N	7	46	Co	0.2	1.5
P	3	44	Mo	0.2	1.5
K	7	113	B	0.2	1.5
Ca	14	6130	Se	0.6	0.3
Mg	2	113	Cl	10	1
S	3	42			

The most recently reported study was from France by Seralini, et al., strictly following European standards for research on rats fed genetically engineered corn (maize). This was a two-year study, the first such study of this length. Most industry studies are conveniently ninety-day studies and the adverse consequences of these studies are underreported or ignored. This study evaluated feeding the rats a diet of 11 percent genetically engineered corn grown with and without the herbicide RoundUp applied to the corn as well as non-GMO feed with RoundUp at 0.1ppm in the water and a control group.

Seralini recorded mammary tumors appearing starting in the fourth month of the study in both male and female rats. He reported that all rats receiving the GMO corn diet died two to three times more than controls and more rapidly. Females developed large mammary tumors sooner and almost always greater than controls. Males additionally exhibited liver congestion and necrosis 2.5 to 5.5 times higher than controls. Males presented four times as many large palpable tumors than controls and 600 days earlier than controls.

It is important to note this study shows that RoundUp in the water ALSO caused significant pathology at very low dosage similar to that pathology caused by the genetically engineered corn.[6]

Two-year feeding study in rats given either NK603 RoundUp-tolerant genetically modified maize, cultivated with or without RoundUp, and roundup alone, at levels permitted in drinking water and GM crops in the United States. Seralini, et al., Food and Chemical toxicology 19 Sept. 2012.

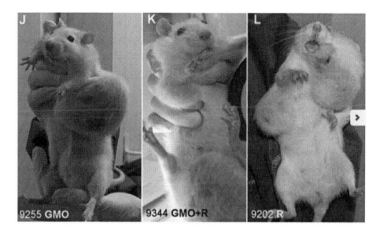

Research to be published in the journals *Neurotoxicology* and *Ecotoxicology* done by Hussein Kaoud at Cairo University's faculty of Veterinary Hygiene with nine groups of rats and mice fed potatoes, corn, grapes, and tomatoes containing 10 percent genetically engineered and 90 percent non-genetically engineered foods. Four weeks into the study, Kaoud observed shrinkage of kidneys, change in liver and spleen, malignancies appeared, kidney failure, and hemorrhages in the intestine; learning and memory were seriously altered. Death rate of babies from mothers fed the GMO diet increased by 35 percent overall with 50 percent dead after three weeks and what babies were born were smaller.[7]

Kaoud also observed that the babies from mothers fed genetically engineered corn had a death rate of 35 percent, were smaller and 50 percent died within three weeks. At Monufiya University, plant pathologist Mohamed Fathy fed genetically modified corn to goats and sheep, which caused them to have liver and kidney effect equal to Kaoud's observation on rats and mice. (*Egypt Independent*, Monday 13 August 2012)

Seralini, et al., evaluated nineteen studies of mammals fed with commercialized genetically modified soybean and maize which represent, per trait and plant, more than 80 percent of all environmental genetically modified organisms (GMOs).

Several convergent data appear to indicate liver and kidney problems as end points of GMO diet effects in the above-mentioned experiments. This was confirmed by our meta-analysis of all the in vivo studies published, which revealed that the kidneys were particularly affected, concentrating 43.5 percent of all disrupted parameters in males, whereas the liver

was more specifically disrupted in females (30.8 percent of
all disrupted parameters).[8]

---

1   Smith, Jeffrey. "Genetically Modified Soy Linked to Sterility, Infant
    Mortality in Hamsters" Huff Post Green. April 20, 2010 12:32 PM
    http://www.huffingtonpost.com/jeffrey-smith/genetically-modified-
    soy_b_544575.html

2   "New Study Links Genetically Engineered Corn to Infertility." No-
    vember 12, 2008
    http://www.organicconsumers.org/articles/article_15588.cfm

3   Medical-biological investigations of transgenic potatoes, resistant to
    the Colorado beetle (under agreement with Monsanto Co.) Russian
    Academy of Medical Sciences, Institute of Nutrition Moscow, 1998.
    Signed off by VA Tutelian, Deputy Director. Physiological, bio-
    chemical and morphological investigations in rats. Full Report 275
    pp, including raw data.
    http://www.democraticunderground.com/discuss/duboard.php?az=vie
    w_all&address=389x229295

4   Rothschild, Mary. "Purdue Scientists Dispute Anti-GMO claims."
    February 26, 2011. http://foodsafetynews.com/2011/02/purdue-
    scientists-refute-anti-gmo-claims/

5   Hartzler, Bob and Mike Owen. "Use Facts to Make Glyphosate and
    Glyphosate Resistant Crop Decisions." Department of Agronomy,
    Iowa State University.
    http://www.extension.iastate.edu/CropNews/2011/0225hartzler.htm

6   Seralini, et al. Long-term toxicity of a RoundUp herbicide and a
    RoundUp-tolerant genetically modified maize. *Food and Chemical
    Toxicology*. 19 Sept. 2012.

7   Irina Ermakova: Influence of genetically modified soya on the birth-weight and survival of rat pups. Proceedings of the Conference "Epigenetics, Transgenic Plants & Risk Assessment" http://www.oeko.de/oekodoc/277/2006-002-en.pdf

8   Gilles-Eric Séralini, Robin Mesnage, Emilie Clair, Steeve Gress1, Joël Spiroux de Vendômois, Dominique Cellier. "Genetically modified crops safety assessments: present limits and possible improvements." Séralini et al. Environmental Sciences Europe 2011, 23:10. http://www.enveurope.com/content/23/1/10

Chapter 5

The Human Connection

It is concerning that digestive problems in human have and continue to increase since the introduction of genetically engineered crops into the animal and human food chain.

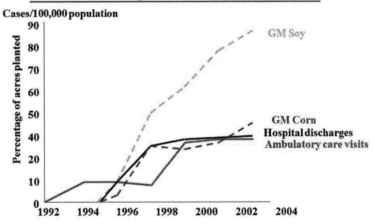

Inflammatory Bowel Disease, USA

The same trend has been observed in Canada especially in children. A study done by Rajani and colleagues at Stollery Children's Hospital observed that celiac disease in children increased elevenfold between 2003 and 2007.[1]

It is very concerning that the incidence of inflammatory bowel disease in the general population is on the rise. "The incidence and prevalence of inflammatory bowel disease (IBD) are increasing with time . . . "[2]

Is there a direct correlation between genetically engineered food consumption and inflammatory bowel disease? All the animal feeding studies show significant bowel inflammation attributed directly to the GE feeds. It would seem logical that the same consequence would befall humans consuming these pro-inflammatory materials.

Those who understand epidemiology know that association does not necessarily mean causation; so technically, I cannot say that the genetically engineered foods are causing the increase in bowel diseases in humans. Yet, when we have multiple species animal studies that DO show causation repeatedly and 100 percent of the time, we must take the association of GMOs and human illness very seriously. As the endocrinology society states regarding endocrine disrupting pesticides, we must apply the precautionary principle.

We must stop the feeding of genetically engineered foods to animals and people. We are now in the third and fourth generation of junk food diets and the second and third generation of glyphosate and genetically engineered crops. Each generation becomes weaker and weaker from this degeneration of the food chain. There is no accident that the latest generation is expected to live a shorter live than its parents.

---

1   Seema Rajani, Hien Q Huynh, MD, and Justine Turner, MD PhD.
    "The changing frequency of celiac disease diagnosed at the Stollery
    Children's Hospital." Can J Gastroenterol. 2010 February; 24(2):
    109–112.

2   Science Daily January 4, 2012.
    http://www.sciencedaily.com/releases/2012/01/120104135402.htm

Chapter 6

Horizontal Gene Transfer and Viral Wildcats

Another issue with genetically engineered crops is that of horizontal gene transfer from the foreign infective gene complex of the food product to indigenous gut bacteria. This horizontal gene transfer permanently alters the consumer's gut flora. The net consequence of this horizontal gene transfer to our own gut flora is permanent endogenous pro-inflammatory antigenic production, transfer of antibiotic resistance to gut flora and consequent production of pro-inflammatory antigens.

One human study in Canada proved this horizontal gene transfer to occur. One type of genetically engineered crop is the Bt sweet corn. This corn has had a gene complex infected into every cell of the corn plant so the plant produces the *Bacillus thuringiensis* insecticide toxin in every cell of the plant.

This protein is called Cry1(b) 93 percent of pregnant women had this protein in their blood and 8 percent of their fetuses. Most concerning was the fact that the quantities found in the blood was much greater than could be accounted for by the amount supplied by the diet alone. Horizontal gene transfer of this protein occurred to the endogenous gut flora and Cry1(b) was being produced within the gut. This is a significantly toxic foreign protein.[1]

An extensive Australian animal study (three species) showed that animals fed the Cry1(b) protein developed pathological intestinal liquefaction and their behavior resembled those of the most acute autistic characteristics. The researcher has subsequently been threatened and intimidated for reporting this study and presenting it for publication.

Additional concern arose with a recent finding by a European Food Safety Authority scientist that the viruses associated with genetically engineered crops lives on for years. The EFSA scientist discovered Gene VI, an independent virus gene overlapping with the naked cauliflower mosaic virus (CaMV) 35S promoter (commonest virus for driving gene expression in GM crops).

Keep in mind that foreign gene materials inserted via genetic engineering technology do not have natural codons in the receiving cells that turn these genes on or off as occurs in natural cells. Biotech engineers must attach an activator, a virus to the gene complex in order for it to get expressed in the cell and ultimately in the plant.

In 1999, CaMV 35S was shown to enhance horizontal gene transfer/recombination, thus, create new viruses, activate old ones and trigger CANCER in animal and human cells. "There is new evidence suggesting that the CaMV 35S promoter may indeed enhance the multiplication of disease-associated viruses including HIV and cytomegalovirus through the induction of proteins required for transcription of the viruses."[2]

---

1   Aris, A., Leblanc, S. "Maternal and fetal exposure to pesticides associated to genetically modified foods in Eastern Townships of Quebec, Canada." Reprod Toxicol. 2011 May;31(4):528-33. Epub 2011 Feb 18.
    http://www.fondazionedirittigenetici.org/fondazione/files/allegatonews27aprile11numero2.pdf

2   Editors. Hazardous Virus Gene discovered in GM Crops after 20 Years. Science in Society #57, Spring 2013. http://www.i-sis.org.uk/AnnouncingScienceinSociety57.php?printing=yes

Chapter 7

The GMO Trend

It is getting nearly impossible for the general consumer to avoid the pro-inflammatory genetically engineered food components in the diet. This is a critical time in viability of both our food chain and our health. Healthcare providers must get proactive in educating their patients to avoid genetically engineered food components.

We must get labeling of foods containing GMO food components so that consumers can avoid them and protect themselves from these disease-causing components. These components include corn, soybeans, canola (canola oil), and cottonseed (oil), and every animal fed such components. This includes chicken, eggs, pork, beef, and milk from animals fed genetically engineered feed. Only organically grown animals are not allowed to be fed such feed. There are a growing number of animal farmers avoiding genetically engineered feeds, but few of these are labeled as such. Genetically engineered foods truly need to be labeled with a skull and cross-bones insignia.

Over 70 percent of all corn, cotton and soybeans grown in the U.S. as of 2010 were genetically engineered. This means that unless the food product is labeled "non-GMO" or "organic" it will contain some or all genetically modified product.

This trend is spreading around the world, just follow the money. Politicians are eagerly holding out open palms for industry greasing and the "promises" for "high-tech" jobs, farm sustainability, and feeding the world. The company Kool-Aid tastes much better with monetary flavoring. March 2013: Congress, in passing the appropriations bill, attached a rider, H.R. 933, that gives genetic engineering companies free range to put GMO crops into the food chain with no proof of safety (animal studies already show they are UNSAFE) nor can they be halted by Federal injunction.

Further, the Arkansas Rice Growers Association is very con-cerned that this opens the door for Monsanto to sell "RoundUp Ready" GMO rice. Already the American rice market has been hurt from Bayer Crop Science's GMO rice that was shipped to the EU by Riceland Food Cooperative. The EU rejected the rice and American rice growers had to bear the burden of a rejected rice crop. Even the non-GMO hybrid rice varieties produced by Rice Tech are not wanted by the world markets, especially Latin America. H.R. 933 put the onus on the public to prove the products are unsafe.

The fundamental fallacy of genetic engineering of crops as already mentioned is that nutrition is the true variable for healthy, pest-free, disease-free, sustainable food production. It is nutrition that actually determines both the genetics and the expression of those genes.

For decades scientists put forward the "one gene—one trait" model for genetic modeling. The Human Genome Project, a multimillion dollar project to map the human genome was intended to map this "one gene—one trait" model of the human with the subsequent intent to develop genetic "cures" to all diseases.

Entire industries have sprouted and sucked in investors with the promise of windfall profits from "cures" to diseases. Like the dot com boom and bust, this "biotechnology" industry is built on false premises, worse perhaps on false "science." To the modeling scientists' dismay, the long-believed model turned out to be false.

As it turns out, the gene itself, sitting on a chromosome in the nucleus of every cell functions more like the musical score for possible cell function than the director/conductor of cell function. In other words, the gene is only a component of the outcome of cell function and replication. For example, consider a musical score, the written piece of music. The conductor reads and interprets the musical score. Depending upon his or her training, philosophy, and personality, the musical score will be differently interpreted. Further, the orchestra made up of many different instruments and many different musicians with different talents and personalities. Their interpretation and execution of the musical score will vary with variations of the musicians.

Take the potential variations in conductors coupled with the variations in the musicians and the musical score may not even be recognizable to the original writer. The New York Philharmonic orchestra's output will be much different than a group of jazz musicians, which will be much different than a junior high school orchestra.

Take the music score for "Roll Over Beethoven" played by the Electric Light Orchestra compared to Avalon. In cells, it is the accompanying proteins in the cell and nucleus that determine how the gene information will be interpreted and expressed, when it will be expressed and to what extent. The same gene in a different cell will code for a completely different outcome. The same gene in the same cell at a different time or under different conditions will code for a completely different outcome.

Further, the gene has been found to be multidimensional, not just a slot on the chromosome. This means that the components that make up a gene can and are spread around the chromosome, not in one neat and tidy slot as originally thought.

This has great implications for "genetic engineering" because there are so many variables that determine what will be ultimately the gene expression. When the technician infects a cell with a foreign genetic unit, the process does not occur as one would insert one ink color cartridge for a different color cartridge. All the identified and unidentified collateral proteins that actually direct and determine the gene expression are ignored.

The consequence is a "third wheel" so to speak in the mix. It is like a ball and chain attached to the gene complex, which takes extra energy to accommodate. Further, because there are uncountable numbers of potential collateral proteins at any one time and place that actually induce gene expression, the outcome consequences can neither be predicted nor controlled. Stability is lost and aberrant products are inevitably produced.

This is the probably consequence of the L-tryptophan "contamination" of the late 1980s. An aberrant, unpredictable amino acid or protein compound, toxic, was produced in the midst of the L-tryptophan by the genetically engineered bacteria used at Showa Denko.

Yet further, the infecting genetic complexes of genetic engineering are foreign protein and virus complexes. It is a given that even half way healthy mammalian immune systems will attack such complexes. That is the job of the immune system. Seventy percent of the mammalian immune system resides in the digestive system. It only holds to reason that digestive system inflammation would occur and it does occur universally with the introduction of genetically engineered "foods" into mammalian diets.[1]

Dr. Mae-Won Ho has published several articles and a couple books on epigenetics, genetic engineering and related biophysics topics. She is a respected and extensively credentialed biochemist with post-doctoral research in human biochemical genetics at University of California at San Diego and further at the University of London. She is currently visiting Professor of Biophysics at the University of Catania, Sicily. Her insight and explanations are timely.

> "Toxic agents in the environment were found to scramble genome sequences to produce new transcripts linked to a range of chronic illnesses such as Gulf War Syndrome, CFIDS, and leukemia."

> "Nutrition and environmental toxins (not the genes) are the greatest physical determinants of generational health/experience/behavior. Social experiences are equally influential."

"The experience of one generation can modify genes passed on to the next via a variety of mechanisms that blur the distinction between epigenetic and genetic."

"The genome is fluid and dynamic, and impossible to pin down; the actions are predominantly in the 'hidden' parts of the genome that don't code for proteins, especially in epigenetic processes in response to the environment."

"Genes are proving to be fragmented, intertwined with other genes, and scattered across the whole genome."

"Coding sequences of different proteins frequently overlap. Regulatory signals are similarly scattered upstream, downstream, within the coding sequence or in some other distant part of the genome. Which exons are recruited to make specific proteins depends entirely on the environmental contexts."

"Epigenetics has put an end to genetic determinism; but by no means supports environmental determinism. The hallmark of epigenetic inheritance is its dynamism and plasticity. Although the environmental epigenetic influence persists for varying periods of time, and can be transmitted across generations, it can also be reversed, or changed further by altering the environment in an appropriate way."

"Epigenetics confirms that the causes of ill health are overwhelmingly environmental and social and must be addressed by appropriate policies."

Mae-Won Ho. Institute of Science in Society. www.i-sis.org.uk

The entire point here is that our problems are not rooted in the genetics. We don't have plant disease and insect problems because of genetics. We don't have weeds because of genetics. We don't have drought, famine and yield loss because of genetics. We have all these things because of inept human management of the farm. Every one of these issues is corrected with presently known farm management and national science. It is not any more complicated than that.

---

1   Genetic Explanations: Sense and Nonsense by Sheldon Krimsky and
     Jeremy Gruber and Epigenetics: How Environment Shapes our Genes
     by Richard C. Francis.

Chapter 8

The Deadly Bedfellow of GM Crops

There are two ways to be fooled. One is to believe what isn't true; the other is to refuse to believe what is true.

—Soren Kierkegaard (1813–1855)

In this case glyphosate and GMOs have been touted as safe when they are horrendously toxic which pundits, including Poison Control, refuse to acknowledge despite a plethora of literature citations proving it so.

Hand in hand with the increase of genetically engineered crop use has been the exponential increase in the use of glyphosate; the dark bedfellow of GMOs. This increase use of glyphosate has resulted in an exponential increase in birth defects, cancer, and other maladies. Despite the documented toxic effects of glyphosate cited in the most recent scientific literature, Poison Control continues to cite 1983 industry claims that glyphosate is virtually harmless and advises callers to the Poison Control toll-free number as such. The following is a list of studies published over the past seven years showing glyphosate, the active ingredient in RoundUp, to be a very toxic chemical not just to animals, but directly to humans in doses observed in drinking water and spray drift.

Direct Toxicity of Glyphosate

Rate (ppm)	System affected	Reference
0.5	Human cell endocrine disruption	Toxicology 262:184-196, 2009
0.5	Anti-androgenic	Gasner et al, 2009
1.0	Disrupts aramatase enzymes	Gasnier et al, 2009
1-10	Inhibits LDH, AST, ALF enzymes	Malatesta et al, 2005
1-10	Damages liver, mitochondria, nuclei	Malatesta et al, 2005
2.0	Anti-Oestrogenic	Gasnier et al, 2009
5.0	DNA damage	Toxicology 262:184-196, 2009
5.0	Human placental, umbilical, embryo	Chem.Res.Toxicol. J. 22:2009
10	Cytotoxic	Toxicology 262:184-196, 2009
10	Multiple cell damage	Seralini et al, 2009
10	Total cell death	Chem.Res.Toxicol. J. 22:2009
All	Systemic throughout body	Andon et al, 2009
1-10	Suppress mitochondrial respiration	Peixoto et al, 2005
	Parkinson's	El Demerdash et al, 2001
POEA, AMPA even more toxic		Seralini et al, 2009

EPA Federal Register Listing: 13ppm for animal feed as of May 2011; sweet corn 3.5ppm and poultry meat at 0.1ppm.

A recent article in *Entropy* 2013, 15(4), 1416-1463 titled, "Glyphosate's Suppression of Cytochrome P450 Enzymes and Amino Acid Biosynthesis by the Gut Microbiome: Pathways to Modern Diseases by Anthony Samsel and Stephanie

Seneff shows the " . . . documented effects of glyphosate and its ability to induce disease, and we show that glyphosate is the "textbook example" of exogenous semiotic entropy: the disruption of homeostasis by environmental toxins"[1]

An article in the *Journal of Hematology & Thromboembolic Diseases* by Belin Poletto Mezzomo, et al., "Hematotoxicity of Bacillus thuringiensis as Spore-crystal Strains Cry1Aa, Cry1Ab, Cry1Ac, or Cry2Aa in Swiss Albino Mice" showed that the protein used in genetically engineered crops targeting insects is, in and of itself, carcinogenic. It induces leukemia in laboratory mice.[2]

Glyphosate has recently been proven to have estrogenic activity and induces breast cancer by affecting estrogen receptors.[3] There are numerous literature citations over the past several years showing glyphosate to be teratogenic, carcinogenic, genotoxic, and endocrine disrupting at concentrations much less than the EPA approved spray rates. I have chosen to actually give excerpts from many of the literature citations in the following because there is a plethora of industry spin, deception, diversion, and outright denial of toxicity or scientific concern.

Academics, paid by industry, frequently will deny most of these citations even exist. One such report titled, Report from the first National Meeting of Physicians in the Crop-Sprayed Towns is a treatise from Argentina reporting on the consequences to the local labor towns in the soybean farming areas taking statistics from hospital and clinic birth records in these areas.

> "It is crucial to acknowledge the fact that, together with the increase in cancer and birth defect cases in the mentioned areas, the use of pesticides also increased exponentially since the introduction of transgenic crops. . . . In 1990, 35 million liters . . . this year we will be spraying the fields with over 300 million liters . . . "

> . . . 3,011,000 births in the United States, between 1996 and 2002. . . . Results: The seasonal pattern (spring) showing an increase of pesticides in water coincided with a higher rate of various congenital birth defects in infants whose mothers' LMP was during spring months, a correlation that is statistically significant.

> The report further elaborated on pesticide research around the world. "Widge, at the University of Ottawa . . . 31 studies . . . Childhood leukemia was associated with pregnant mothers' occupational exposure to pesticides, OR = 2.09, IC 95 percent,

1.51 to 2.88 (over twice as much more probabilities to develop leukemia than in the control group)."

The entire report can be accessed at http://www.reduas.fcm.unc.edu.ar/wp-content/uploads/downloads/2011/10/INGLES-Report-from-the-1st-National-Meeting-Of-Physicians-In-The-Crop-Sprayed-Towns.pdf

A follow up meeting of physicians occurred in 2011 for the second National Meeting . . .

" . . . reduction in the average age and height" of residents in crop-sprayed towns . . . " In addition, "birth defects, mutagenesis, miscarriages, depression and suicide, disorders of the central nervous system and other neurological pathologies; disabilities, spina bifida, lupus, leukemia and other types of cancers; chloracne and other skin problems; asthma, allergies, and other respiratory and lung-related problems; male sterility and impotence; hormonal disruption and other hormonal disorders; diminished childhood development; prolonged febrile syndrome without focus; children's increased vulnerability to pollutants; anemia, multiple sclerosis, cerebral ischemia, death."

That report is available at http://www.i-sis.org.uk/Pesticide_illnesses_and_GM_soya.php

http://www.reduas.fcm.unc.edu.ar/declaration-of-2nd-
meeting-of-physicians-of-sprayed-and-fumigated-towns-and-
villages/

The following are just a few of the over 145 peer-reviewed paper exposing the serious toxicity of glyphosate, the active ingredient of RoundUp. See Appendix for an additional listing.

Glyphosate-based herbicides are toxic and endocrine disruptors in human cell lines.[3]

Glyphosate formulations induce apoptosis and necrosis in
human umbilical, embryonic, and placental cells.[4]

Time- and dose-dependent effects of RoundUp on human
embryonic and placental cells.[5]

> " . . . a negligible amount acting during months or
> years can be more disordering in a durable way
> (and even with transgenerational effects) than a
> short exposure to a high dose."

> " . . . the concept of 'threshold,' without taking du-
> ration into account, is not really scientific."

> The World Health Organization (WHO) definition
> of an endocrine disruptor (ED) that the European
> Union (EU) adopted in 1999: " An endocrine dis-
> ruptor is an exogenous substance or mixture that

alters function(s) of the endocrine system and consequently causes adverse health effects in an intact organism or its progeny or subpopulations."[6]

Glyphosate and RoundUp cause birth defects in frog and chicken embryos in doses far lower than those used in agricultural spraying.

Humans have the same developmental mechanisms as frogs and chickens. Malformations seen in the experimental embryos similar to the human birth defects reported in GM soy-growing areas of South America.[7]

" . . . we found genotoxic effects after short exposure to concentrations that correspond to a 450-fold dilution of spraying used in agriculture. . . ."[8]

At lower nontoxic concentrations of RoundUp and glyphosate (1 ppm), the main endocrine disruption is a testosterone decrease by 35 percent.

Leydig cells are exposed to this kind of environmental doses (Acquavella, et al., 2004) because 1 ppm was found in human urine and thus was present in blood. When 10 ppm of G are given to rats, half was still found in plasma 15 h later (Anadon, et al., 2009).[9]

" . . . three food microorganisms (Geotrichum candidum, Lactococcus lactis subsp. cremoris and Lactobacillus delbrueckii subsp. bulgaricus) widely used as starters in traditional and industrial dairy technologies. The presented results evidence that RoundUp has an inhibitory effect on microbial growth and a microbicide effect at lower concentrations than those recommended in agriculture. RoundUp is always more potent than glyphosate, and in all cases, toxic from levels 10 to 100 times below the lowest agricultural uses (10,000 ppm). G. candidum and L. cremoris are more RoundUp sensitive than L. bulgaricus.[10]

Cry1Ab can induce cytotoxic effects via a necrotic mechanism . . . RoundUp is cytotoxic by inhibition of mitochondrial respiration activity, far below agricultural dilutions (around 200 times less) with an LC50 of 57.5 ppm.

RoundUp is antiandrogenic from 0.5 ppm, below toxic levels and close to human serum levels (0.1–0.2 ppm in Acquavella et al., 2004).[11]

"R (RoundUp) at doses far below those used in agriculture and at levels of residues present in some genetically modified food and feed. The prevention of such phenomena took place within 48 h with the plant extracts tested, with success rates ranging between 25-34% for the E293 (embryonic human kidney) intoxicated by RoundUp, . . . 71% for the HepG2 (embryonic human hepatic). By contrast, after intoxication, no plant extract was capable of restoring E293 (kidney) viability within 48 h, however, two medicinal plant combinations did restore the Bisphenol-A/Atrazine intoxicated HepG2 up to 24-28%. . . . plant extracts were not capable of preventing radiolabelled glyphosate from entering cells; . . ."[12]

"Industry (including Monsanto) has known since the 1980s that glyphosate causes malformations in experimental animals at high doses."

"Industry has known since 1993 that these effects could also occur at lower and mid doses."

"The German government has known since at least 1998 that glyphosate causes malformations."[13]

Research by a German university has recorded glyphosate in urban professionals from four German cities at levels five to twenty times the legal limit for drinking water.[14]

Glyphosate in Human Urine (Urbanites) & Dairy Cows

City	No.	Male	Female		Dairy	Glyp*.	Dairy	Glyp.
1	44	10.3*	6.1		A	9	E	37
2	22	16.0	2.7		B	21	F	38
3	19	60.1	8.3		C	22	G	46
4	22	23.5	13.8		D	25	H	102

*ppm glyphosate   *ppm, herd average

Permitted in cereals, soybean, corn = 20 ppm
Permitted in alfalfa = 400 ppm Corn silage = 100 ppm
Toxicity to beneficial GI flora = 0.1 ppm
Long-term toxicity to liver, kidney, etc. tissues = 0.1 ppbillion
Long-term carcinogenicity = 0.1 ppb
Antibiotic to beneficial enteric bacteria = 0.1 ppm

Research in Germany by Monica Kreuger and colleagues draws some concerning links between glyphosate residue in the animal feeds and visceral botulism. Glyphosate kills the natural microbial suppressants of C. botulinium resulting in the proliferation of C. botulinium and release of the botulinium toxin. The concentration of glyphosate in the food necessary to kill the clostridia botulinium organisms is ten times that necessary to kill the beneficials that keep the C. botulinium suppressed. Therefore at low doses of glyphosate residue in the food, systemic botulism poisoning becomes a real threat.

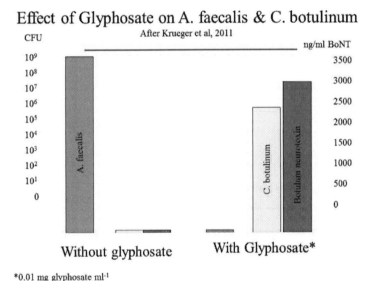

Effect of Glyphosate on A. faecalis & C. botulinum

After Krueger et al, 2011

*0.01 mg glyphosate ml⁻¹

Krüger, M., A. Shehata, J. Neuhaus, T. Müller, M. Kotsch, W. Schrödl. "Chronischer Botulismus des Rindes eine Faktorenkrankheit" (Cow illness from chronic botulism) "Welche Rolle spielt das Totalherbizid Glyphosat?" (What role does glyphosate play?)[15]

A study from several European countries sampling urine from urban dwellers revealed: "...urine samples from volunteers in 18 countries across Europe ... found that on average 44% of samples contained glyphosate..." "All the volunteers who provided samples live in cities, and none had handled or used glyphosate products in the run-up to the tests..."[16]

Proof of glyphosate's selective antimicrobial properties is further exhibited by its August 10, 2010, patent 7,771,736 as an antibiotic/antiparasitic drug. In spite of this patent, many farmers, university professors and industry publicists contend that glyphosate does not kill beneficial microorganism.

It doesn't stop there, however. Not only does glyphosate kill beneficial soil, dairy, and intestinal microorganisms, it results in the promotion of a long list of pathogens in addition to toxic clostridia bacteria mentioned above. The following is a list of known pathogenic organisms increased with the application of glyphosate.

Cercospora spp.

Corynespora cassicola

Fusarium spp.

Fusarium avenaceum

F. graminearum

F. oxysporum f. sp cubense

F. oxysporum f.sp (canola)

F. oxysporum f.sp. glycines

F. oxysporum f.sp. vasinfectum

F. solani f.sp. glycines

F. solani f.sp. phaseoli

F. solani f.sp. Pisi

Gaeumannomyces graminis

Magnaporthe grisea

Botryospheara dothidea

Monosporascus cannonbalus

Myrothecium verucaria

Phaeomoniella chlamy-
dospora

Phytophthora spp.

Pythium spp.

Rhizoctonia solani

Septoria nodorum

Thielaviopsis bassicola

Xylella fastidiosa

Clavibacter nebraskensis

Xanthomonas sterwartii

Marasmius spp.

Below is a list of plants, the disease and the casual pathogen of the disease precipitated as a result of glyphosate use on the soil subsequently growing these crops.

Some Diseases Increased by Glyphosate

Host plant	Disease	Pathogen
Apple	Canker	*Botryosphaeria dothidea*
Banana	Panama	*Fusarium oxysporum* f.sp. *cubense*
Barley	Root rot	*Magnaporthe grisea*
Beans	Root rot	*Fusarium solani* f.sp. *phaseoli*
Bean	Damping off	*Pythium* spp.
Bean	Root rot	*Thielaviopsis bassicola*
Canola	Crown rot	*Fusarium* spp.
Canola	Wilt	*Fusarium oxysporum*
Citrus	CVC	*Xylella fastidiosa*
Corn	Root and Ear rots	*Fusarium* spp.
Cotton	Damping off	*Pythium* spp.
Cotton	Bunchy top	Manganese deficiency
Cotton	Wilt	*F. oxysporum* f.sp. *vasinfectum*
Grape	Black goo	*Phaeomoniella chlamydospora*
Melon	Root rot	*Monosporascus cannonbalus*
Soybeans	Root rot, Target spot	*Corynespora cassicola*
Soybeans	White mold	*Sclerotina sclerotiorium*
Soybeans	SDS	*Fusarium solani* f.sp. *glycines*
Sugar beet	Rots, Damping off	*Rhizoctonia* and *Fusarium*
Sugarcane	Decline	*Marasmius* spp.
Tomato	Wilt (New)	*Fusarium oxysporum* f.sp. *pisi*
Various	Canker	*Phytophthora* spp.
Weeds	Biocontrol	*Myrothecium verucaria*
Wheat	Bare patch	*Rhizoctonia solani*
Wheat	Glume blotch	*Septoria* spp.
Wheat	Root rot	*Fusarium* spp.
Wheat	Head scab	*Fusarium graminearum*
Wheat	Take-all	*Gaeumannomyces graminis*

Fusarium scab

Take-all root rot

Additionally, glyphosate use is causing emerging and ree-merging plant diseases including nutrient deficiency diseases; bark cracking, mouse ear, and 'witches brooms.'

What must be understood is the actual mechanism of action for glyphosate's consequences. It is robbing, stealing or capturing of trace minerals by the process of chelation that causes the problems. Glyphosate was originally patented by Stauffer Chemical Company, U.S. patent 3,160,632, December 8, 1964, as a descaling agent, e.g. chelating agent, to remove scale from boilers or similar machinery. An inadvertent spill at a warehouse revealed the product to have herbicidal characteristics. Monsanto purchased glyphosate from Stauffer Chemical Company and later patented it as a herbicide, and subsequently, as documented above, as an antibiotic. Its "kill" function is by chelation of trace elements.

Greenhouse potted plant studies reveal that in sterile soil, glyphosate only weakens a plant by chelating its manganese, particularly related to the ESPS amino acid pathway, called the Shikimate Pathway; but, does not kill the plant. However, when glyphosate is applied to the same species of plants in regular soil, the plant dies.

The mechanism is that glyphosate weakens the plant by chelating its trace elements making it more susceptible to soil pathogens. Some of the glyphosate is translocated out through the plant roots, killing the plant protective beneficial microbes and promoting the proliferation of resident plant pathogens; thus, the actual kill of the plant is by these subsequent soil plant pathogens.

Adding further fuel to the fire, glyphosate specifically kills those microbes that electrochemically reduce nutrients, such as iron plus 3 reduced to iron plus 2, and promote those that electrochemically oxidize nutrients, such as converting iron plus 2 to iron plus 3. It is the reduced form, iron plus 2, of nutrients that are usable by plants, animals and humans.

% Mineral Reduction in Roundup Ready® Soybeans Treated with Glyphosate

Plant tissue	Ca	Mg	Fe	Mn	Zn	Cu
Young leaves	40	28	7	29	NS	NS
Mature leaves	30	34	18	48	30	27
Mature grain	26	13	49	45		

Reduced:
Yield   26%
Biomass   24%

After Cakmak et al, 2009

% Reduction in Alfalfa Nutrients by Glyphosate*

Nutrient	% reduction compared with Non-RR
Nitrogen	13 %
Phosphorus	15 %
Potassium	46 %
Calcium	17 %
Magnesium	26 %
Sulfur	52 %
Boron	18 %
Copper	20 %
Iron	49 %
Manganese	31 %
Zinc	18 %

*Third year, second cutting analysis; Glyphosate applied one time in the previous year

It is important for the reader to understand that the primary mechanism of action of many poisons is to chelate critical metal cofactors in enzyme systems; thus, rendering the enzyme pathways inoperable. That mechanism, in and of itself, does not necessarily "kill" the plant in the case of herbicides, though it may in the case of bacteria, animals and people.

As for the plant, in the case of glyphosate, originally patented in 1964 as a descaling/chelating agent, it targets manganese in the ESPS enzyme pathway (inhibition of 5-enolpyruvylshikimate-3-phosphate synthase) as ESPS is a manganese-dependent enzyme. This does NOT kill the plant, rather it reduces its immunity. Experiments in sterile soil demonstrate that the glyphosate sprayed plant, a targeted weed, is not killed, only stunted somewhat. The actual "kill" function of the glyphosate application is done as a result of the glyphosate reducing the vigor of the plant, while at the same time enhancing the vigor and virility of the soil pathogens, especially fusarium, and the fusarium (not the glyphosate) infects and actually kills the plant.

This chelating characteristic is what leads to the direct reduction in nutrient levels of all crops sprayed with glyphosate. Most all herbicides chelate metal, but most are focused chelators while glyphosate is a broad-spectrum chelator, robbing all cations within its influence.

Digressing a bit, the mere presence of the infective genetically engineered glyphosate resistant gene in a plant requires the plant to expend more energy just to deal with the foreign machinery. This further reduces mineral metabolism. Considering this fact, yet another process reducing the nutritional value of our food crops plus glyphosate chelating out trace minerals on top of the universally poor farm management practices (already proven to be responsible for the declining nutrient value of our food), is there any wonder the food to-day is so poor, nutritionally; that we have a pandemic of food contaminating pathogens; that resistant disease organisms and weeds now abound around the world; that birth defects and child cancers have increased exponentially in pesticide ex-posed areas; that inflammatory bowel disorders have in-creased in both animals and humans?

Particularly concerning in this discussion is the affect GMOs, glyphosate, and other pesticides are having on children. Childhood allergies, digestive issues, and behavioral prob-lems have and continue to rise correlated to the introduction of genetically engineered foods and the significant increase in glyphosate use. The November 5, 2007, *Newsweek* front cover featured the growing problem of food allergies in chil-dren. The graph below shows the significant increase in childhood autism. I realize there has been significant research on the association between immunizations and autism sub-stantiated by the recent Macaque monkey study done at Uni-versity of Pittsburg showing immunizations caused autism like behavior in baby monkeys.[17] It is true that the increase in childhood vaccines is associated with the rise in autism, I didn't say "causation." I have personally witnessed, in my practice some children become autistic from vaccines, documented on child videos. That is not to say that all children that become autistic due to vaccines or that vaccines cause autism.

One must ask why these children are susceptible and why is the number of susceptible children increasing. The introduction of genetically engineered foods and the significant increase in use of glyphosate on our food has increased inflammation, has further demineralized our food and glyphosate further targets testosterone producing cells explaining the predominance of autism in boys. As already shown, the Cry1(b) protein from GMO crops directly causes autism-like behavior in several species of mammals.

The GMOs and glyphosate put fetuses/children either directly at risk for developing autism or significantly increase the susceptibility for developing autism when some exogenous stressor, such as vaccines, mercury or toxic chemical, comes along and induces autism or at least aberrant behavior. Consider that children in the U.S. are over three times as likely to be on an antidepressant and stimulant and 1.5 to 2.2 times as likely to be on an antipsychotic than children in The Netherlands and Germany.[18]

Doctors treating autism and ADHD today acknowledge that success is much more elusive today than fifteen or twenty years ago. Treatments that were highly successful fifteen years ago just don't have the result today. The illnesses are much more complex today.

Allergies in children is running rampant. The cover story of *Newsweek* magazine, November 5, 2007, "Kids and the Growing Food Allergy Threat," was an expose on this raging problem in America about which the standard medical community has not clue as to the cause.

Allergies are not the only issue raging in our children. Autism continues to expand as evidenced by the following CDC graph from Michigan.

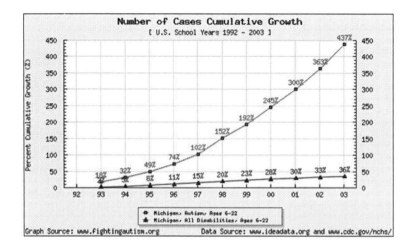

It's not just behavior, allergies, and birth defects that are the consequences of glyphosate and other pesticides. A recent study published in Environmental Research shows a direct relationship between pesticides in the fat of individuals and the development of type II diabetes, another disease that continues to skyrocket in western society. It's not the genes, it's the environment! It's not the "fat gene", the "cancer gene" or the "diabetes gene." It's the toxic, gene-altering/gene expression–altering food environment that shoulders the burden for these increasing trends.

The paper by Arrebola, et al., essentially says that when other known causes of diabetes are taken out of the picture, there is a direct association between the chemical presence and the risk of diabetes. Arrebola, Juan P., et al. "Adipose tissue concentrations of persistent organic pollutants and prevalence of type 2 diabetes in adults from southern Spain."[19]

Summarizing, glyphosate directly chelates trace nutrients, thus reducing trace nutrient levels and immune resistance; kills beneficial microorganisms, promotes oxidizers and pathogens. As was previously cited, glyphosate does this in soil, in plants, in animals, and in food cultures. It is carcinogenic and causes birth defects at concentration much below those used in agricultural sprays.

Why does Poison Control continue to contend that glyphosate is safe? Good question! I had the opportunity to spend a month with the Tampa Poison Control center, officed across the street from Tampa General Hospital. The reason Poison Control continues to state that glyphosate is safe and not worrisome is due to the fact that they continue to cite 1983 documentation provided by Monsanto stating that glyphosate is safe and biodegradable.

The documentation further contends that glyphosate's mechanism of action of blocking the Shikimate amino acid pathway in plants is not found in humans; therefore, there is no worry of toxicity in humans. The problem with this logic is that research since that 1983, especially since 2000, shows glyphosate to be very toxic to animals and humans, is not biodegradable (ruled not to be by the French Supreme Court) and its mechanism of action to be via chelation of trace elements which DOES occur in humans.

We also know now that glyphosate disrupts the P450 enzyme systems of animals. These are critical enzymes involved in the detoxification of xenobiotic chemicals, hormones and drugs. If these enzymes don't function properly, our bodies cannot clear metabolic and environmental toxins nor even the medications taken by prescription.

It has also been well established that many of the industry threatening diseases such as citrus greening and citrus canker and Panama disease in bananas are glyphosate precipitated diseases due to the use of glyphosate sprayed around the trees.

A very important issue regarding glyphosate needs to be addressed. This is its aquatic application. Homeowner associations, lake owners associations, and landscape managers regularly have algae and weed problems in their waterways—ponds, lakes, streams, and canals. The reason these problems exist is first and foremost the fertilizer program applied to the landscape around these waterways.

We have the landscape technology to fertilize and care for turf and landscape plants resulting in greener and better health landscape, up to a 50 percent reduction in water use proven by OBHA in Houston (www.obhaonline.org, weed free and more durable turf, and no nitrogen leaching completely without the use of pesticides. This is where the management needs to start, with the landscape.

Cleaning up the waterways without pesticides is a realistic and long-term solution. Weeds and algae are there because of the run-off of nutrients from the landscape; so stop that first. The nutrients must be cycled by microorganisms in order to reduce the weeds and algae. This is done with two operations. The first is inoculating with beneficial probiotics and the second is proper aeration to keep these probiotics alive. Done properly, the waterways will be clear in a few months, permanently. Two companies I know of address these problems; Tainio.com and CIRCUL8 Systems. Both companies travel around the world solving waterway problems.

The typical approach is applying more and more herbicide; the herbicide treadmill. This is because the cause is not addressed, landscape runoff, and the weeds inevitably become herbicide tolerant or resistant. The more-on principle always eventually fails. Common today is the application of glyphosate-based aquatic herbicides, such as Rodeo and Shore-Klear. Below is the State of California publication on glyphosate safety:

> "Glyphosate rapidly dissipates from surface waters, and soil microflora quickly biodegrade glyphosate into AMPA and CO_2 (Gardner & Grue 1996). AMPA also undergoes rapid degradation to CO_2 in soil (Rueppel, et al., 1977). A review of key documents and studies assessing the acute and chronic toxicity, neurotoxicity, immunotoxicity, and endocrine disruption risks of glyphosate-based herbicides, indicates that non-target organisms are exposed to minimal risk through the use of these herbicides."[20]

The problem is that their citations are all older citations. Since 2002, there are numerous scientific studies that show glyphosate to be very toxic at doses much less than those sprayed on the land. The doses found in wind drift are enough to cause significant problems as already cited earlier in this chapter. Additionally, the industry claim to rapid bio-degradability is incorrect as noted previously.

Glyphosate is carcinogenic and there are numerous claims of cancer nests around the small lakes and waterways in Florida where glyphosate based sprays are applied nearly every two weeks. It is insane! Solve the problem! Clean up the land-scape and then clean up the waterway as described earlier.

There are over 140 citations on the toxicity of RoundUp and/or its active ingredient glyphosate at the end of this book compliments of Dr. Don Huber, Professor Emeratus, Purdue University, Colonel (Ret.), U.S. Army expert in biological weapons threats.

---

1   Samsel, Anthony and Stephanie Seneff. Entropy 2013, 15(4), 1416-1463.

2   Mezzomo BP, Miranda-Vilela AL, Freire IdS, Barbosa LCP, Portilho
    FA, et al. (2013) Hematotoxicity of Bacillus thuringiensis as Spore-
    crystal Strains Cry1Aa, Cry1Ab, Cry1Ac or Cry2Aa in Swiss Albino
    Mice. J Hematol Thromb Dis 1: 104. doi:10.4172/jhtd.1000104

3   Thongprakaisang, S., Thiantanawat, A., Rangkadilok, N., Suriyo, T.,
    Satayavivad, J., "Glyphosate induces human breast cancer cells growth
    via estrogen receptors," Food and Chemical Toxicology (2013), doi:
    http://dx.doi.org/10.1016/j.fct.2013.05.057

4   Gasnier C, Dumont C, Benachour N, Clair E, Chagnon MC, Séralini
    GE.Toxicology, 2009 Jun 17. [Epub ahead of print].

5   Benachour N and Seralini, GE. Chem Res Toxicol, 22: 97-105, 2009.

6   Benachour N, Sipahutar H, Moslemi S, Gasnier C, Travert C, Séralini
    GE. Arch Environ Contam Toxicol, 53:126-133, 2007.

7   Chapter 1, Advances in Medicine and Biology. Volume 29. Nova Sci-
    ence Publishers. Inc. 2012

8   Chem Res Toxicol. (2010) 23: 1586-1595.

9   Arch Toxicol. 2012 Feb 14.

10 Toxicology in Vitro 26 (2012) 269–279.

11 Curr Microbiol. DOI 10.1007/s00284-012-0098-3. Springer. Published
    Online 24 February 2012.

12 R. Mesnage,a,b E. Clair,a,b S. Gress,a,b C. Then,c A. Székácsd and G.-
    E. Séralinia,b* Cytotoxicity on human cells of Cry1Ab and Cry1Ac Bt
    insecticidal toxins alone or with a glyphosate-based herbicide. J. Appl.
    Toxicol. 2012. (wileyonlinelibrary.com) DOI 10.1002/jat.2712

13 Céline Gasnier1,2, Claire Laurant3, Cécile Decroix-Laporte3, Robin
    Mesnage1,2, Emilie Clair1,2, Carine Travert1, Gilles-Eric Séralini1,2.
    Defined plant extracts can protect human cells against combined xeno-

biotic effects.* Gasnier et al. Journal of Occupational Medicine and Toxicology 2011, 6:3 http://www.occup-med.com/content/6/1/3

14   Antoniou, Michael et al. "RoundUp and birth defects: Is the public being kept in the dark?" Earth Open Source, 2011. http://www.scribd.com/doc/57277946/RoundUpandBirthDefectsv5

15   Brändli D, Reinacher S. "Herbicides found in Human Urine." Ithaka Journal 1/ 2012: 270–272 (2012). www.ithaka-journal.net. Editor: Delinat-Institute for Ecology and Climatefarming, CH-1974 Arbaz. www.delinat-institut.org, www.ithaka-journal.net. ISSN 1663-0521

16   Tribe, Michelle. "Weed killer found in human urine across Europe." *Friends of the Earth Europe*. http://www.foeeurope.org/weed-killer-glyphosate-found-human-urine-across-Europe-130613 and "Determination of Glyphosate residues in human urine samples from 18 European countries." June 6, 2013 *Test Facility* Medical Laboratory Bremen, Haferwende 12, 28357 Bremen, Germany. *Sponsor* BUND, FoE https://www.foeeurope.org/sites/default/files/glyphosate_studyresults_j une12.pdf

17   Infant Macaque Monkeys Given Standard Doses of Vaccines Develop Autism Symptoms. April 27, 2012. http://prof77.wordpress.com/2012/04/27/infant-macaque-monkeys-given-standard-doses-of-vaccines-develop-autism-symptoms/

18   Institut für Bakteriologie und Mykologie, 2011.

19   Child and Adolescent Psychiatry and Mental Health. Science Daily. September 25, 2008, 2:26.

20   Environmental Research. Volume 122, April 2013, Pages 31–37. http://www.sciencedirect.com/science/article/pii/S0013935112003210

21   Monheit, Susan, CDFA-IPC. " Glyphosate-Based Aquatic Herbicides An Overview of Risk"

http://ceres.ca.gov/tadn/control_manage/docs/glyphosate_aqua_risk.pdf

Chapter 9
An Emerging Disease Agent

As if all of these toxic effects from GE crops and the increased use of pesticides, especially glyphosate, were not enough, a "new" biomolecular matrix infective agent has come to our attention. This agent, the size of a virus, is not living so it cannot be killed; yet, it has been applied to Koch's Postulate for infective agents and conforms to it.

It was initially found, via scanning electron microscope, in the placentas of spontaneous abortions in thoroughbred horses in the late 1990s. More recently it has been found in association with infertility and spontaneously aborted fetuses in cattle and humans as well as seemingly a virulence factor in plant diseases in the past classified as nuisance infections, now devastating pandemics including Goss's Wilt in corn and Sudden Death Syndrome in soybeans. It appears to be directly correlated to glyphosate application and the feeding of genetically engineered crops.

Infertility is a common consequence of this new entity. The U.S. Cattlemen's Association Statement to Congress July 24, 2002:

> "Cattle ranchers are facing some puzzling—and, at times, economically devastating problems with pregnant cows and calves. At some facilities, high numbers of fetuses are aborting for no apparent reason. Other farmers successfully raise what look to be normal young cattle, only to learn when the animals are butchered that their carcasses appear old and, therefore, less valuable.
>
> "The sporadic problem is so bad both in the United States and abroad that in some herds around 40-50 percent of pregnancies are being lost.
>
> "Many pesticides and industrial pollutants also possess a hormonal alter ego.
>
> "The viability of this important industry is threatened."

"Testimony of the Ranchers-Cattlemen Action Legal Fund," United Stockgrowers of America, to the Senate Agriculture Committee, Washington D.C., July 24, 2002.

Hoard's Dairyman, November 2011, express similar concerns in an article by Jenks Britt, D.V.M. and Fernando Alvarez, M.V.Z., "Why are so many cows losing pregnancies?

Losing up to 20 percent of pregnancies is not acceptable."
Out of six herds and around 7,000 cows, between 25 and 27
percent of pregnancies were lost to unknown causes.

This infective entity has been verified in Iowa, Illinois, Ken-
tucky, Michigan, Nebraska, North Dakota, South Dakota, and
Wisconsin. It has been found in soybean meal, silage, corn
grain and silage, soybean plants infected with Sudden Death
Syndrome, manure, soil, spontaneously aborted placental tissue from animal and humans, amniotic fluid, semen, stomach
contents, eggs, and milk. It has also been isolated in the my-
celium of Fusarium solani fsp glycines.

Is this new infective agent a bedfellow of glypho-
sate/RoundUp? Perhaps since glyphosate predisposes plants
to infective agents, kills beneficial microorganisms that protect the plants and roots. Glyphosate does the same to animals
via chelating vital trace minerals and killing protective gut
flora. Glyphosate enhances the growth and explosion of
pathogenic organisms.

This so-called "new entity" from all information and testing
available, appears to be actually a "biomolecular matrix" very

much like nanobacteria sanquinium featured in Scientific American May 2002, discussed in an article by Miller V., et al., Mayo Clinic, Journal American College of Cardiology, March 2002. Finnish scientists, Neva Ciftcioglu, Ph.D. and Olavi Kajander, M.D., Ph.D. are credited with the initial discovery of nanobacteria sanguinium in 1988.

Professor Charles Bryce described it as "a microcrystalline form of hydroxyapatite complexed with exogeneous biological macromolecules, including DNA and protein." Alternative View on the Putative Organism, Nanobacterium sanguineum. Professor Charles F. A. Bryce, Braids Education Consultants, Edinburgh EH10 6NZ, Scotland Nanobacteria were discovered in 1988 by the Finnish scientists, Neva Ciftcioglu, Ph.D., and Olavi Kajander, M.D., Ph.D., as a contaminant that killed cell cultures.

Around the year 2000, a university professor looking for the cause of numerous unexplained spontaneous abortions occurring in the regional horse population, found an unidentified "entity" under scanning electron microscope that resembled nanobacteria sanguinium. It satisfied Koch's Postulates and seemed to be associated with every spontaneously aborted placenta he analysed. Further study found this same "entity" in the placental tissue of cattle and humans, genetically engineered corn and soybeans and diseased corn and soybeans. Extensive analyses suggest that this "entity" is perhaps a zinc-based hydroxyapatite biomolecular matrix, a "sister" to nanobacteria sanguinium.

There is great debate whether this represents a new, unidentified nano-organism, the same debate as took place with nanobacteria sanguinium, because analyses can find DNA, RNA, apparent cell membrane material, and various minerals. Such findings are explained by the presence of a biomolecular matrix. Consider the scaffolding or basic mineral structure of any living cell.

Over time, due to demineralization of our food chain—and particularly we find this thing in demineralised plants, this fundamental scaffolding demineralises. Then along comes a very strong universal chelator, glyphosate. This chelator removes just enough additional mineral that the cell dies. What remains is a mineral scaffolding with many open electrical charges left over from the minerals being removed.

This scaffolding or matrix itself is a chelator and draws to it anything with a charge including minerals, organic molecules, membrane components, RNA, DNA, etc. As it does so, cells around it dies as a result and the matrix appears to replicate but it is really growing much like a crystal will replicate in solution once a "seed" crystal forms. As this matrix proliferates it appears to be "pleomorphic" due to its expansion. In this expanding morphism, it can trap prions, viruses, bacteria and yeast acting as a transporter, a vector and infector. It is still non-living and therefore cannot be killed.

Think of the difference between living coral and dead coral; between living bone and dead bone. The hydroxyapatite matrix remains though it is non-living. This hydroxyapatite-like bio-matrix can be calcium based, zinc based, iron based, or most any cation mineral based. Lab experiments with zinc nanoparticles show that a similar looking biomolecular matrix can be synthesized in the lab.

It is a consequence of demineralization, initially from poor farming practices with the final blow from the presence of glyphosate that pushes the demineralized cell over the threshold. This is not what most people want to hear as they want something they can kill, something for which they can develop some new chemical weapon. Since it cannot be killed it is indeed a very serious invading "entity." It appears to enhance disease organisms rendering them more serious. Actually, it is simply chelating materials from cells, thus making them more susceptible to disease organism invasion.

The correction is the same as the prevention of this bio-molecular matrix. Nutrition is the answer. This must be full spectrum nutrition, especially trace minerals, applied in adequate quantity to first overcome the chelation inactivation of minerals by the bio-matrix and/or glyphosate and second, supply the necessary mineral to heal the cell. Providing adequate nutrition, in the first place, prevents this bio-matrix from forming. Prevention is the most important. On the other hand if we cannot get therapeutic levels of nutrition into the living organism adequate to overcome the thievery of the bio-matrix, we must starve it. Work done with horses aborting because of the bio-matrix showed that significantly limiting feed intake in the pregnant mares resulted in successful term pregnancies.

Ultimately the demineralization of our food chain as a result of demineralization of our soils is the answer to whatever this "entity" may be and why it manifests as well as the many significant consequences of modern agriculture. The following is an electron microgram of this bio-matrix. Note the middle picture is a bacteria with the bio-matrix peppered around it. It is indeed very small. It has been found in all genetically engineered crops and non-GMO crops where RoundUp/glyphosate has been applied.

Two years ago, Dr. Don Huber, doing what he was previously commissioned to do by the Department of Defense with the Armed Forces Medical Intelligence Center as Assistant Director, and at the time of the letter, doing his work as Coordinator of the USDA Plant Disease National Recovery Program, sounded the alarm to the Secretary of Agriculture imploring the Secretary to order research into this potentially disastrous infective agent. He was subsequently permitted to go to Washington with a group of scientists to present his/their case.

After a potent and detailed presentation accompanied by over 135 peer-reviewed articles on this whole mess (GMOs, glyphosate, bio-matrix), Dr. Huber was told by the Secretary's office that when he had peer-reviewed literature to share, their office would consider the case. In case you missed what I just said, AFTER Dr. Huber presents over 135 peer-reviewed articles, the Secretary's office said they would listen if he presented peer-reviewed literature. If fact, when Dr. Huber pointed that out to the Assistant Secretary that he had just presented peer-reviewed literature, the statement was repeated. In other words, "don't confuse me with the facts. . . ." His letter was leaked to the press and a massive campaign has been waged against Dr. Huber to discredit his credentials and reputation.

Dr. Huber's concern was that all preliminary evidence suggested a disaster waiting to happen; consequently, more researchers and facilities were needed to explore this "entity" to determine what it really was, what its characteristics were, what were its disseminations in the food chain, and what would be done about it if it proved to be as serious as he feared. He is a scientist, sounding the alarm as he was originally trained to do and at that time commissioned to do. The administration's response was to discredit the messenger rather than investigate the message.

The inconvenient truth is that "modern agriculture" with its genetically engineered crops, RoundUp/glyphosate/phosphonate herbicides, and demineralization of our soils and crops has precipitated a potentially disastrous infective biomolecular matrix; that could possibly collapse the entire "modern ag" façade. Below is an electron microscope photo of this matrix.

Scanning Electron Microscope Image, 20,000 X

Size relative to a bacterium

Mag:20000 WD:15   1 µm

Chapter 10

The Modern Agricultural Complex: Concocter of the "Green Revolution"

Keeping in mind that most pesticide poisons are chelating agents lends an answer to the manifestation of the "mad cow" disease. BSE, Bovine Spongiform Encephalopathy, a prion disease that gained international press a number of years ago, stirred up considerable fear among consumers, led to the mass slaughter of thousands of animals and provided an open platform for any number of theories. The most accepted contributing cause was the feeding of animal protein back to cattle and sheep. Understand that cattle and sheep are absolute herbivores; they only eat plants when left to their own devices.

Seeking to push for more production at cheaper costs, feed companies and farmers decided to accept the practice of force-feeding these animals as if they were cannibals. The prions, believed to be associated with BSE, were readily carried in the animal protein feed and transferred to the consuming animals allegedly causing subsequent BSE in these animals. It doesn't take a rocket scientist to understand that feeding a ruminant animal—a herbivore—meat, making it a cannibal is going to lead to problems of some sort.

Conveniently not mentioned in the investigations of the causes of BSE was the fact that cattle and sheep farmers were applying organophosphate insecticides to these animals in treating them for lice and flies. Organophosphates are copper chelators. Once absorbed into the animal, these poisons would chelate out the copper from the nervous system (the poison was applied along the back bone of the animal). Without copper, the prion structures, which are naturally occurring structures within the nerve cell structural matrix, subsequently precipitated out to be transferred in the meat protein products from animal to animal. Appropriate nutrition on the farm is the prevention needed to stop BSE!

Humans are very good at creating new problems for themselves, unnecessarily. Nutrition is the foundation of health and production in agriculture. All the "challenges" claimed by the agricultural-war-industrial (AWI) complex are created and/or invented by this complex itself. Nutrition is not highly profitable and certainly if appropriate nutritional management leads to health, it is even less profitable for this AWI complex. As consumers, the most important concept to grasp is that food quality is truly about nutritional density, nutritional value of the food. That is achieved through appropriate farm management. The higher the nutritional value of the food, the better it tastes, the better is looks, the better it yields, the better it digests, the better it stores, the better it is for the environment, the more efficient it is to grow per unit of production.

Certainly all the issues discussed above are concerning, even devastating for society in human terms. Know that they are all preventable with appropriate farm management. To encourage this type of farm management, the consumer holds the strongest hand. Money is the motivator and the consumer votes daily at the grocery store with his/her money. This demand determines what will eventually get grown. Regardless of what the AWI complex rhetoric, the truth eventually comes out at the grocery store.

The consumer has the power to change the system, to get the system to produce better quality food, food that is truly nutritionally sound and satisfying. What the consumer is willing to spend his/her money to buy determines the demand. The market will always seek to satisfy the demand. It does take some time to shift the inertia of the AWI complex, but money is still the driver. The market has attempted to confuse and even deceive the consumer by all the rhetorical expressions of quality.

Unfortunately, most consumers have no clue what a good vegetable or fruit should taste like because they have never had a good—nutrient dense—vegetable or fruit. People have accepted a norm of taste and aesthetics that is sub-par, that is they have no experiential reference for how food should really taste or look. How often have you eaten a meal, thought to be nutritious, only to feel stuffed but not satisfied; only to be hungry a short time after leaving the table looking for something else to eat? This is a normal response for lacking nutrient.

The food just consumed did not provide the body with the nutrition it was craving so even though it provided filler, it did not provide sufficient nutrition—vitamins, minerals, amino acids, antioxidants. Again, this is due to our severely faulty agriculture. I know this assertion sounds questionable; after all, America has the most sophisticated, most technologically advanced military in the world; America has NASA; America has, supposedly, the most technologically advanced medical system in the world. How is it possible that the most productive and efficient (so we are told) agricultural industry in the world could be so far off the mark?

Very simply, agriculture has become enamored by all the bells and whistles of modern technology and so profitable from perpetuating the extension of the "war machine" into a civilian business model, that it has completely lost site of the fact that agriculture is (or certainly should be) first and foremost about the production of food for people.

Today, farming is more about commodity production, as if producing automobile engines, fenders or seats, than about providing the sustenance for a healthy, productive society. Most farmers have completely lost the appreciation that they are supposed to be producing food for people and that the quality and contamination of that food directly affects the health of not only every consumer that eats the products, directly or indirectly, which they produce, but also that it is their own families or future families that consume this production. Often we hear farmers state that it matters little the quality, because they are not paid for quality. It matters not for the quality because they sell it down the road to some obscure end user.

Certainly there couldn't be anything hazardous, dangerous or concerning about anything they, the farmers, sell because EPA, USDA and/or FDA have directly or indirectly approved everything that eventually gets to the consumer. It is just all those fanatical "greenies" people that haven't a clue where their food comes from that are muddying the waters for no scientific or realistic reason. Why, these chemical weapons (pesticides, also fondly called "crop protection agents") are so safe you can drink them, in fact, many people have drank them, allegedly, without any adverse consequences. They're so safe you can buy them at any home improvement or gardening store and use them in your home and around the yard. Besides, the toxicologists and industrial hygienists mantra is "the dose makes the poison" meaning that these chemicals are used in such small doses on food crops that they are way below anything problematic for the consumer. Most importantly, we would all starve to death if it weren't for modern farm chemicals.

It is hard to imagine humans survived up to the 20th century without all these farm chemicals necessary to "protect their crops."

This is such a ridiculous discussion. Why would any sane person apply POISON to his/her food and contend that it is just fine, the dose is low. As the physicists and geneticists have proven, dose is actually secondary to timing of embryonic development and what appears to be a low risk dose for an adult in the short term is actually a huge dose for the fetus at particular stages of development.[1]

Further, the additive and/or synergistic effect of any one or more of these chemicals combined with other chemicals is never taken into account.[2]

All the industry testing used for EPA/FDA approval is done with one chemical at a time, in a vacuum, as if this would be the only chemical exposure in a completely pristine, sterile environment/living system. An excellent example is glyphosate versus RoundUp. Glyphosate has been shown to be teratogenic, genotoxic and carcinogenic alone, but its toxicity is multiplied many times when combined in the mix called

RoundUp, whose active ingredient is glyphosate plus added adjuvants.

The entire discussion really comes back to nutrition, specifically nutrient content/density of the food, the vegetable, fruit, nut, or grain. What is meant by this statement? Two things are meant: 1) The higher the nutrient content of the plant product as a result of the appropriate growing technique, the less that crop is affected by insect pests and diseases. In fact, it is possible to increase the nutrient density of the crop to the point that there is NO, yes NO insect or disease pressure WITHOUT any, nadda, none, no pesticide being applied, of any kind, synthetic or "organic." 2) The higher the nutrient content of the food the healthier will be the consumer, potentially to the point that no pharmaceutical drugs are "needed" to maintain health.

This level of professional farming that produces nutrient dense food doesn't sell much poison so the universities don't get the "research" grants to perpetuate the training of students to use more poisons. People and animals consuming such nutrient dense foods get fewer if any illnesses so the drug companies sell fewer drugs, the doctors do fewer surgeries, the medical equipment companies sell fewer devices and the universities get less grant money to teach the students to use more drugs and devices. Sickness is simply more profitable, better for businesses, and better for government tax collection than health.

The proverbial statement from the mouthpieces of this "system" is that insects and disease are going to attack crops if the insects and disease organisms are in the area, period. Crops are there food sources so they are going to eat. There is just one little slip of the tongue or actually deletion of a key descriptive adjective in this contention. SICK crops are the food sources of insects and disease organisms. Insects, in particular, have different digestive systems than do humans and animals. I will bet the reader never knew or thought about that. Life-sustaining food to the insect is different than life-sustaining food for human or animal.

The insect's digestive system is designed to digest simple elemental nutrients like mineral nitrogens, simple sugars, and simple amino acids which are abundant indirectly proportional to the overall nutrient integrity of the plant, e.g., the higher the nutrient density the more complex the elements, sugars and amino acids; thus, the fewer there will be simple elements, sugars and free amino acids, and, subsequently, the less attractive to the insect.

Francis Chaboussou, a French biologist working at the French Ministry of Agriculture, wrote a book in 1985, describing and explaining this very principle. He called it "trophobiosis." It was first published in French, then Portuguese and, finally, in English about fifteen years later. A priori, insects are merely Nature's garbage crew designed and commission with the task of removing those plant materials from the food chain that do not adequately nourish mammals.

Understand that when a plant's nutritional density/balance reaches a given threshold or above, it is NOT attractive to insect pests because it does not contain the simple food components which their digestive systems can digest, so they leave it alone. It is as concrete as why a cow will not eat road kill but will eat grass. Interestingly, if you have two patches of grass pasture side by side, the cow, if given the choice, will go to the more nutritionally enriched pasture first to eat.

It matters not whether the farmer is conventional or organic in his practices. What matters is the nutrient integrity of the crop. It is important for consumers to know that though the organic produce may have less or no pesticide residue because of the farmer following "organic" production constraints, the organic produce may not have more nutrient value than the conventional produce. The key is nutrient management by the farmer, organic or conventional. Organic production simply means the farmer did not use unapproved materials per USDA NOP (National Organic Program) standard. It does not mean he or she actually got anymore nutrient into the crop.

How might the consumer evaluate produce for nutrient density? As mentioned earlier, check its taste and shelf life. One can also check its smell, its weight per volume—higher is better. One can send it off to a lab but that is expensive. A simple tool to use is the refractometer.

2) It is the nutrition that is disrupted by the many endocrine disruptors in the environment, particularly and specifically in this discussion, glyphosate, the active ingredient in RoundUp. Glyphosate chelates, steals, sequesters, inactivates (or whatever term one chooses to use to describe the act of reducing

plant available mineral) trace mineral nutrients. This demin-
eralizing effect weakens the plant by disrupting the plant's
ability to manufacturer fats, proteins and carbohydrates to the
fullest extent needed by the plant. In this weakened, "anemic"
state, the plant is ideal prey for disease organisms and insect
pests. It is amazing that university "scientists" will vehe-
mently deny that insects, diseases and weeds are present due
to poor agronomic nutritional management (the very nutritional management they espouse), yet the very mechanism by
which their subsequent touted chemical work is by reducing
nutritional status of the target—plant, insect, weed. There is a
simple explanation for this seemingly dichotomous behavior—follow the money.

---

1   Braw-Tal R. Endocrine disruptors and timing of human exposure.
     Pediatr Endocrinol Rev. 2010 Sep:8(1):41-6.
     http://www.ncbi.nlm.nih.gov/pubmed/21037543

2   Kortenkamp, Andreas. "Ten Years of Mixing Cocktails: A Review of
     Combination Effects of Endocrine-Disrupting Chemicals." Enviro
     Health Perspect. 2007 December, 115(S-1):98-105.
     http://www.ncbi.nlm.nih.gov/pmc/articles/PMC2174407/

Chapter 11

Food Quality and Brix

Brix is the term named after Antoine Brix, a French vintner in the mid-1800s desiring to more practically evaluate the amount of sugar in grape juice for the purpose of making wine. Today the brix scale is used additionally by the food industry for measuring the amount of sugars in fruit juices, soft drinks, and sugar products. It is measured with an instrument called a refractometer calibrated in percent sucrose in water as brix.

Refractometers are used in medical labs to test for salts, sugars, albumen, and specific gravity, each having a different calibration depending upon the desired material to be tested. The actual mechanism of function of the refractometer is that a drop of liquid is placed on the prism, the cover piece is closed over the liquid and the tester looks through the eyepiece. Light, coming through the prism, through the liquid, is bent to different amounts depending upon the quantity and characteristic of products in the liquid.

The net result of the light bending forms a line across the scale seen in the eyepiece. The number seen where the line crosses the scale is the brix value cited. The scale is calibrated using water and sucrose. One pound of sucrose in 99 pounds of water give a brix of 1, 10 pounds in 90 pounds of water give a brix of 10, and so on.

Fruit sap is more complex than simple sucrose in water. There are sugars, amino acids, salts, and other materials in the sap making up the total dissolved solids in that sap. All these materials will affect the refractive index of this sap, thus the brix. As a general rule of thumb, the higher the brix value of plant, fruit or vegetable sap, the higher the dissolved solids, the higher the nutrient value, the healthier the plant and of course the sweeter the taste. Refractometers used commonly by farmers, gardeners, and consumers have a scale from 0 to 32 brix.

Dr. Carey Reams, several decades ago, developed a chart correlating food quality to brix reading for poor, average, good, and excellent. Most food products need to be 12 brix or above to be considered good. Exceptions would be grapes, which must be above 18 to be considered good, while the sap of the vine from which these grapes were taken would need to be 12 or above to be considered good. Tomato vines at 12 or above brix will not necessarily produce tomato fruit at 12 brix or above. A good tomato fruit would be 8 brix or above, excellent would be 12 or above. Sweet corn ears must be 22 to 24 brix to be considered good while the plant sap must be 12 or above.

An interesting occurrence will generally be observed when the plant sap reaches 12 brix or above, 24-7, meaning all the time. Insects and disease will not be interested in the plant. As mentioned previously, at some threshold of health improvement, the plant is no longer digestible by these "garbage sanitation engineers" and are not attacked by them, AND NO PESTICIDE, ORGANIC OR SYNTHETIC, IS NEEDED. This is the quality of food we need to maintain our health. A full brix chart can be downloaded from www.highbrixgardens.com.

Consumers would do well to purchase a refractometer and keep a log of the brix readings of all the fruit and vegetables purchased noting which brands have the highest brix values, correlating the brix to taste, storability, cooking experience and ultimately eating and digestibility. Use this information to train yourself how to purchase better quality produce and to demand from the produce market, better quality food. Remember, consumers vote with their dollar every time they make a purchase.

Keep in mind that the refractometer, like any instrument, has its potential misgivings. It measures what is present. It is up to the operator to interpret the measurement. If an apple is tested fresh off the tree, found to have a brix of 14, put into storage and tested again 2 months later having a brix of 15 and a month later having a brix of 16, has the apple gotten better, more nutritious over these months in storage? The answer is no.

What has happened is that some of the starch has converted to sugar over time AND the apple has dehydrated somewhat over this time, yielding a higher concentration of sugars and dissolved solids in the juice; thus, the increasing brix readings. The brix charts are appropriate for fresh off the tree, vine, out of the field produce. Once it has been stored, processed, gassed, or adulterated, the chart values must be amended to take these changes into consideration.

One of the best judges of whether the brix value is in the excellent range AND the produce is excellent quality is the presence or absence of insect and/or disease organisms consuming the produce. Truly high quality produce will naturally be FREE of insect pests and disease organisms WITHOUT spraying poisons to kill them. Confusing the issue for the consumer is the fact that farmers and retailers contend the food is good or excellent quality produce because it is free of these natural "sanitation engineers." They don't tell the consumer the only reason the produce is free of these "pests" is because the food was sprayed with poison to kill the "pests."

I say again, truly high-quality food does NOT need to be sprayed with poison to kill the insect pests and disease organisms because they aren't present in the first place. Spraying poison on food to kill the pests so the farmer and retailer can claim the food is high quality is like painting a rusty old car and claiming it is a new car because you cannot see the rust.

If you poison the rats feeding on the garbage in the ally next to your house so you don't see rats, does this mean you no longer have garbage present in the ally? Of course not.

This is such a fundamental concept that consumers need to understand. High-quality food is naturally free of pests because high-quality food for people is not acceptable food for pests. Their digestive systems can't handle it. The pests are designed to consume defective, poor quality, nutritionally inadequate crops to recycle them back to the soil and prevent these inferior plants from being consumed by mammals. If the mammals are allowed or forced to consume these inferior foods, the mammals (that's us) become sick from nutritional deficiencies. This is exactly what we see in society, especially consuming the standard American diet; heart disease, obesity, diabetes, cancer, behavior problems, drug resistant infections.

It is so convenient, intellectually numbing and industrially profitable to keep all things sick. Growers/farmers simply follow scripted actions on the farm, each of which includes some direct or indirect accompanying synthetic chemical sale. No real thought is needed; no conscience is required regarding the consequence to the consumer because all the production from the farm is just a commodity disappearing down the road in a truck.

Sick soils grow sick crops produce sick animals and people. At every juncture from the soil to the human consumer, this model creates its own "demand" for more poison, more intervention, more chemical warfare all keeping the cash flow going from the consumer to the chemical weapons' manufacturing and sales network, to the intellectual prostitutes at the universities who are paid to "research and verify" the "science" of this chemical war on nature and to the government directly in the form of sales tax and indirectly in the form of political campaign funds to be sure the policy model continues.

History shows that 20 percent of any population consists of the real innovators, movers and shakers, and early adaptors. The next 60 percent are late adaptors; go with the crowd, status quo folks. The last 20 percent are the diehard sticks in the mud, "don't confuse me with the facts" group that eventually just dies off and never gets it. This latter group is the 20 percent that perpetuates the current model of agricultural production and medicine.

It is the initial 20 percent, the movers and shakers that will read this book; that will seek true science; that will "get it." This 20 percent is a huge buying base and as it sets the tone at the grocery store with its purchasing dollar (euro, pound, yen . . .) Truly high-quality food is not only naturally free of pests and disease, but also tastes better, stores better, digests better, looks better, and is naturally free of toxins and poisons; plus, growing this high quality food actually regenerates the environment, sequesters carbon, uses less natural resources, is more profitable to the farmer, and is forever sustainable. Once the consumer realizes this model to be true and realistic, he or she can and will make it happen via voting at the grocery store with purchasing demand.

Keep in mind that "organic" growing does NOT guarantee better food. Philosophically it should; however, organic growing standards are procedural based upon a list of approved and disapproved products the farmer uses to grow the crop. This standard uses conventional soil and tissue testing parameters to "approve or disapprove" when and how much a farmer may apply of an approved product/nutrient, which only guarantees the status quo for nutrient density/quality.

The fact remains that a farmer can get organic certification if he or she does nothing nutritionally but let the crop grow "naturally." How quaint, how special that seems. Nature will send in the "garbage crew" to recycle this junk so the "organic" farmer will apply "approved organic" pesticides/fungicides to kill these insect and disease critters. The net result is food no better and perhaps lower in nutrient density than conventionally grown food. ONLY if the "organic farmer" manages the crop with adequate nutrition to raise the brix to the excellent range resulting in a crop healthy enough that insect pests and diseases naturally avoid the crop, will this "organic food" be truly high quality. This latter approach is what the concept of "Beyond Organix" is all about. This is an organization founded by myself, Stan Kadota and Mark Nakata of Frenso, California depicting certified organic food crops that additionally were nutrient dense and high brix.

Outcome is the only thing that matters in this discussion on food quality. That outcome is nutrient value/density. Regardless of the procedure, protocol, mechanism, location, or philosophy used to grow the crop, the higher the nutrient density/quality will result in a higher brix reading, which means the food provides better sustenance for the consumer, period.

This nutrient density principle is only a challenging concept for people to grasp because, for decades, the chemical weapons industrial complex has continuously told the consumer that chemical weapons (pesticides, fungicides, herbicides) are perfectly safe sprayed on our food; that we all would starve to death without them; that "science" is on their side.

Along that line of thinking then, every consumer should add another condiment shaker to their kitchen table next to the salt and pepper. This third shaker should be filled with a mixture of pesticides most commonly used on our food certainly to include glyphosate, pyraclostrobin, organophosphate, and organochlorine. Of course, we would have it dosed to the EPA/FDA standard. At every meal, the consumer would add this "crop protection agent" cocktail mix to his or her food to "maximize the food quality" as the industry and farmer tell us all these chemical weapons do for our food. How ridiculous is that concept, but industry, university professors, and farmers continue to puppet it to consumers.

Regularly the AWI (Agriculture War Industrial complex claims that American agriculture is the best in the world, produces the cleanest, most pristine, safest food available anywhere. Then there are the "naturally grown," "organically grown," "biodynamically grown," etc., claims and labels on various food products. In some cases these products are better than the standard, run-of-the-mill food products, but in other cases they are no better or even worse.

The problem with all this rhetoric is that it is just that, "rhetoric." None of these presentations or claims, whether from the AWI complex or the alternatives is about actual food nutrient density/value. All their standards are procedural, meaning that the farmer or processor simply followed some prescribed procedure, checked the right boxes, and followed protocol. The actual value of the product itself from a nutritional perspective is never addressed. Outcome, regarding nutritional value/density, is not considered; only outcome from a procedural compliance perspective is considered.

This means that conventionally grown, pesticide sprayed food commodities, fruits, and vegetables may be just as nutritious as the "naturally grown," "organically grown," "biodynamically grown" products; and in some cases they are just as nutritious. Some people will say that that may be true, but there will be pesticide residue on those foods grown with pesticides. That is probably true most of the time, but not all the time because it is impossible to truly have an environment that is pesticide free in today's world due to drift, pesticides in the rain water, soil residues and farmers cheating with the procedures. Again, this debate is just rhetoric. We need to eat food for nutritional intake.

What really matters about food is the nutritional value, not the procedure under which it was grown. Poor farm management is still poor regardless whether the farmer is a conventional chemical weapons type of guy or whether he or she is a natural or organic weapons type of guy or gal. Low-brix crops are still poor quality regardless of what procedure the farmer followed to grow them and should be left to Nature's garbage crew to recycle.

With that in mind, the consumer can purchase a refractometer, calibrated in brix for checking the "sugar" content of various foods. A picture of a typical consumer refractometer follows. They range in price from $50 to $250 for the type shown or $300 range for a digital model.

When fruit and vegetables are purchased and brought home, squeeze some of the juice onto the refractometer and take the reading. This reading is then compared to the standard chart found at www.highbrixgardens.com. This chart was formulate by the late Dr. Carey Reams several decades ago and correlates very closely with the actual nutritional value of the produce.

I suggest keeping a log book recording the brand; store that sold the produce; defining characteristics, such as color, shape, odor, weight per size/volume; taste; how the rest of the group stores; any cooking characteristic noted, such as significant shrinkage, odd odor, etc. Note how fast the produce turns brown after peeling; the faster it browns, the lower the antioxidant level. Over time, the consumer will gain an appreciation for the characteristics of fruits and vegetables, e.g., weight per size or volume, color, shape, fragrance, etc., at the store to better make selections for the more nutritious produce. Keep in mind that the longer the produce sets on the shelf the more dehydrated it gets, which will give a "false" increase in the brix. The brix of the fresh product at picking is what the chart standard is based upon.

This process puts control back into the hands of the consumer. Regardless what the seller or farmer say about how pristine and wholesome his/her produce may be, the brix level is the best man-on-the-street judge of it true nutritional quality. If the brix of the fresh product is in the excellent range, it is what you want to buy. It if is in the low range, you pass. Demand that your grocery produce managers buy their produce based upon brix levels. Remember it is the consumer's purchasing dollar that casts the deciding vote. Continue to buy junk and that is what the grocery will supply.

The counter-offensive to this problem is knowledge. Brix testing is a simple home test available to every consumer. It is simple, quick, and relatively accurate for evaluating fresh fruit, vegetable and milk quality. Generally, the higher the brix reading of the juice from the fruit or vegetable and the milk, the higher the nutrient values of the product; the better the taste and the longer the shelf life.

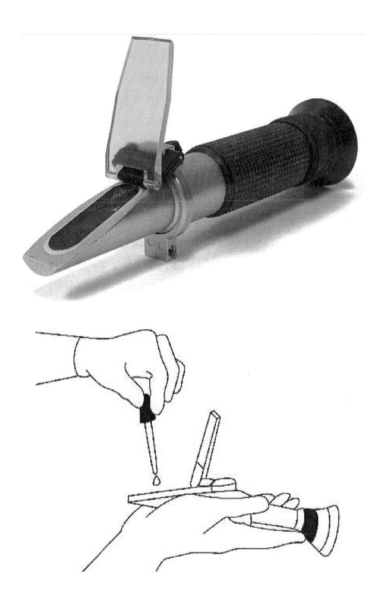

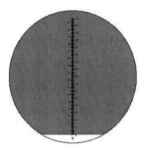 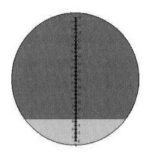

*Water on Lens
to calibrate*

*Refractometer Lens
Simulation with plant
sap: Plant likely to be
attacked by insects
and or disease when
brix this low, 5.5*

Preliminary research findings suggest that high-brix fruit does
not raise blood sugar to the degree that low-brix fruit does.
This should be common sense. Higher brix fruit has more
complex carbohydrates and higher trace nutrient content. This
has significant ramification regarding diabetes, glycemic index, insulin resistance and nutritional value for the body.
New Zealand research by Mr. Peter Floyd, founder of eCO-
GENT, shows that the higher the pasture brix, the higher the
profit per acre. Higher brix grass means that the cow will get
more nutrients for each mouthful of grass she eats. Whether
the pasture is low-brix or high brix, the cow can only take so

many mouthfuls of grass per day, so common sense would suggest that the more nutrient she gets with every mouthful the healthier she will be and the more milk she will produce.

So how do we get higher brix pastures, fruits, and vegetables? We get it by applying sound biological science on the farm. Interestingly enough, appropriate farm management that produces high-brix, nutrient dense food, additionally, by default, addresses all the environmental agendas.

The following list refers to consequences that automatically occur when appropriate farm management is employed:

- Cleans up the environment by sequestering nutrients, eliminating erosion, detoxifying chemicals, regenerating habitats including water
- Reduces cost per unit of production of food
- Sequesters, rather than exhausts, carbon dioxide
- Eliminates the NEED for chemical weapons and GMOs
- Provides sustainable food production for the world
- Provides solid financial basis for small farmers, worldwide
- Provides true food security/safety
- Provides real medicinals for doctors to treat patients

- Reduces inflammatory triggers in the food and environment

Now that we have discussed the four primary or core issues of the Food Plague (Food Demineralization, GMOs, Glyphosate and Biomolecular Matrix) threatening our survival, we can cover some of the peripheral food quality topics that so often garner debate.

Chapter 12

. . . and The Rest of the Story

There are many issues plaguing our food system; more specifically, the "green revolution" food system. The core issues discussed previously in this book represent what I consider the most immediate/urgent threat to human health and survival and the health and survival of our planet as a human and animal sustaining unit.

This is not to make light of the list of issues to be discussed in the following chapters, only to impress the point that unless the declining nutrient density of our foods, the genetic engineering of our foods and the new bio-matrix infective agent are reversed, eliminated and prevented in that order respectively, the following issues are really just kindling on an already raging fire of destruction.

First and foremost, if the declining nutrient value of food is reversed starting in the soil, on the farm, in the field, then many of the subsequent discussion issues naturally fall away on their own accord without much, and in some cases, no deliberate intervention.

Chapter 13

It's In the Water

Water is a vital nutrient and one of the most contested natural resources around the world. Wars have been fought over water and the issue of water rights, distribution, and quality will ever be with us. Regarding drinking water, it has been suggested that the recommended daily intake should be near half one's weight in ounces or in other words a 200-pound person should drink about 100 ounces, about 3 quarts (liters), of water per day. That is a lot of water for some people particularly those that don't want to have to use the toilet. Nonetheless, this is a good quantity for maintaining health. I personally drink bottled spring water. Yes there are the issues of the plastic, the quality of the spring from which the water came, what additives have been put in the water by the bottler and of course what contaminants such as pesticides, drugs, hormones, and fertilizers may be found in the water.

Distilled water is a good place to start and then add back some alkaline minerals. There are those that claim that distilled water washes out one's body minerals. Good luck with that one. Show me the clinical studies that prove it. The kidneys regulate what comes out in the urine. They are not open tubules that will erode with the flow of water through them.

When we drink water, it goes into the digestive system where, if distilled water, it can solubilize minerals in the food in the gut. This water is absorbed into the circulatory system, first going through the liver and then the rest of the body, including the kidneys. These same people will claim that we must drink "natural" water with mineral to replenish the body. They are assuming that this "natural water" has a perfect balance of minerals just for us. Good luck with that one, too. It will have whatever minerals the rocks had as the water passed over them, which are not necessarily what every person on the planet needs.

We can use some of the minerals in water, but certain minerals in water have been clinically attributed to kidney stone formation. The debate rages on. I would certainly prefer not to have water stored in plastic, but when the choice is either drink water in plastic bottles or don't drink any water, I will drink water in plastic bottles. Most municipal water supplies are loaded with chlorine and fluoride, both toxic and at least stressful to the body, plus other undesirables such as iron, drugs, and pesticides.

I recommend that in the home we run a reverse osmosis unit for all drinking and bathing water followed by running the water through the Pursanova water device. This device restores the life force to the water. Experiments using water treated with the Pursanova device on plants show distinct plant growth and health improvement and, with plants, there is no placebo effect. One company I work with, FHR, uses Pursanova treated water in all their liquid fertilizer products.

Chapter 14

Antibiotics and Growth Hormones

I again recently traveled to New Zealand and Australia. I really enjoy my trips down under. The people are wonderful, friendly, and industrious. It had been $4^{1}/_{2}$ years since my last visit and I was quite disappointed by what I experienced happening in New Zealand. New Zealand has the international reputation of being the poster child for "clean, green, and pristine." No more!

About six years ago I had a private meeting with the then Minister of Agriculture. He seemed like a cheerful chap, political and chatty right up to the point where he explained to me that even though over 70 percent of New Zealanders did not want genetically engineered crops in their country, he and his administration knew better than the public. He would see to it that genetically modified crops were brought into New Zealand and made a part of their "world-class" agriculture.

My visit this time to New Zealand confirmed that not only
did the minister get his wish, but New Zealand may very well
be the fastest polluting developed country in the world. The
Minister for the Environment stated in an article that over half
of New Zealand's lakes and streams are no longer safe for
SWIMMING! New Zealand sheep farmers dip their sheep
four or more times per year in toxic insecticides and inject
them with growth hormone to get them to have multiple
births. They have been "forced" to use a combination of der-
quantel and abomectin because of resistant parasites. Further,
since the sheep are so weak, they don't cycle well so farmers
use Ovastim and Androvax to get them to cycle and increase
twinning. Yummy New Zealand lamb, NOT.

Their dairy farmers now produce milk that is two to three
times the milk urea nitrogen level as U.S. milk, feed the cows
the antibiotic Rumensin daily and EU regulators found the
soil nitrogen inhibitor antibiotic, dicyandiamide (DCD) in the
milk. Fonterra claims they have now stopped allowing the use
of DCD on dairy pastures. Dairy farmers are also importing
palm kernel and distillers dried grains (from genetically engineered corn) to feed their dairy cows ever more moving to the
American dairy "feedlot" model.

Only consumer demand and better farmer education will change this deadly, destructive path upon which these folks have embarked.

Growth hormones are also quite prevalent in animal operations to increase weight gain and growth. Drugs, such as Synovex, contain progesterone and estradiol benzoate, are implanted in young animals and feedlot animals to stimulate increased weight gain and fat accumulation. Ever wonder why children are so much larger today and why obesity is such a problem? Perhaps all these feminine synthetic hormones are contributing.

The reason farmers use these goes back to the same issue as before, poor nutrient value of the feed so the animals don't grow rapidly so they are given synthetic growth stimulants to force the weight gain; and then people eat this meat.[1]

BST, Bovine Somatotropin, is a genetically engineered synthetic growth hormone given to dairy cows to force them to product more milk without improving their diet. This of course burns out the cow sooner, but she is seen as an expendable, depreciable item in the scheme of things anyway, so farmers care little about her health consequence. Canadian health authorities refused to approve BST after reviewing safety studies feeling it and the consequent milk to be unsafe for human consumption. The U.S. FDA ignored these warnings. This is just another reason to seek "organic" milk, and particularly A2 organic milk.[2]

A common practice for chicken farmers is to feed the drug Roxarsone to control coccydiosis and promote chicken growth. It contains organic arsenic, which is supposed to be stable and non-toxic. However, research in 2006 found that " Roxarsone-treated chicken has 'three to four times greater [inorganic] arsenic levels than do poultry not treated with Roxarsone and equally greater than meat from other animals'—levels that for heavy chicken eaters, would be 'greater than the tolerable daily intake recommended by the World Health Organization.'"

The Institute for Agriculture and Trade tested supermarket chicken for inorganic arsenic and found that "nearly three-quarters of the raw chicken breasts, thighs, and livers from conventional producers that were tested carried detectable levels of arsenic."[3]

Another interesting tidbit of information is that egg producers feed annatto to chickens to get the eggs to color. It is a "natural" product so that is not the issue. The issue is that the chickens are so sick and nutritionally deficient that unless some colorant is added to the eggs, the yolks won't color, they would be a sick grey color.[4]

Egg cholesterol is not about the egg. It is about the degenerating, deficient diet fed to the chicken and the stress the chicken experiences in its life. Appropriate feed nutrition, full spectrum lighting, plenty of fresh water, and appropriate space allow chickens to produce eggs with higher omega-3 fatty acids, lower cholesterol, and dark yellow/orange yolks without the need for coloring in the feed.

A 2008 study by U.S. CDC estimated that antibiotic resistant human infections cost a single healthcare institution $13.35 to $18.75 million. One such resistant infection is that of resistant Salmonella; resistant to cephalosporins found is livestock and retail meats as well as humans.

"Studies have shown that use of cephalosporins in food animals can select for antibiotic resistant bacteria, and, in some cases, specific uses of this class of drugs in food animals are associated with higher rates of resistance among human Salmonella infections."

"Following the approval of fluoroquinolones for use in poultry, rate of resistance to this class of drugs among human Campylobacter isolates rose sharply, to more than 20 percent."[5]

" . . . data were collected in 2000, and the rate of notifications of antibiotic resistant cases has more than doubled since then . . ." said Prof. Susan Foster, a co-author and health economist at APUA. "Antibiotic-Resistant Infections Cost the U.S. Healthcare System in Excess of $20 Billion Annually."

http://www.prnewswire.com/news-releases/antibiotic-resistant-infections-cost-the-us-healthcare-system-in-excess-of-20-billion-annually-64727562.html

A recent study from the Maryland School of Public Health along with researchers from Pennsylvania State University and Johns Hopkins Bloomberg School of Public,

" . . . found an immediate and substantial decrease in antibiotic-resistant bacteria on poultry farms that had just switched from conventional to organic practices. And this happened in the very first flock raised organically."[6]

"26.5 million pounds of antibiotics estimated to be used in the United States as feed additives each year—seven times the amount used in human medicine nationwide. The report, Resistant Bugs and Antibiotic Drugs: Local Estimates of Antibiotics in Agricultural Feed and Animal Waste," www.environmentaldefense.org/go/antibiotic.,estimates.

"Studies suggest that people living in areas with intensive use of antibiotics as feed additives are at greater risk of contracting antibiotic-resistant infections," said Ellen Silbergeld, Ph.D., Professor of Environmental Health Services at Johns Hopkins Bloomberg School of Public Health.

http://www.edf.org/news/1st-study-estimated-local-use-antibiotics-livestock-feed-additives-shows-90-estimated-use-conce

"In one study published in the *New England Journal of Medicine* on February 6, 2002, researchers found links that strongly suggested that the people who developed Cipro-resistant bacteria had acquired them by eating pork that were contaminated with salmonella. The report concluded that salmonella resistant to the antibiotic flouroquine can be spread from swine to humans, and, therefore, the use of flouroquinolones in food animals should be prohibited."

"Another *New England Journal of Medicine* study from October 18, 2001, found that 20 percent of ground meat obtained in supermarkets contained salmonella. Of that 20 percent was contaminated with salmonella, 84 percent was resistant to at least one form of antibiotic."[7]

Regardless of the facts of the matter and the Public Health concerns, industry refuses to acknowledge the significance of the problem, the threat to human life, and the reality of organic farmers not needing antibiotics for their animals.

Industry's contention that there exists a "need" for feeding antibiotics is simply fiction. The need is to SELL antibiotics, but the animals don't "need" to be fed antibiotics. Just follow the money. Animals are not born with an antibiotic deficiency. This is a "false" savings for two reasons. First, antibiotics cause "leaky gut" so the animals absorb more undigested, poorly digested, and toxic material, all of which induce inflammation. This inflammation is seen upon inspection of the digestive systems of slaughtered animals at any slaughter house one visits. Inflammation begets fluid retention, hence weight gain and it is what the farmer sells, weight.

Appropriate nutrition would give equal or better weight gain and healthier animals. Second, due to the antibiotic resistance problem and the lessoned animal product quality (meat and milk), public health suffers, costing society billions of dollars in medical expenses. There is no real savings involved, merely diverted and masked costs to the consumer.

The reason feeding antibiotics have gained favor with farmers is one, that the feed is nutritionally degenerated, thanks to farm management as already pointed out; and two, this deficient feed leads to weakened animals and animal immune systems, decline in the beneficial flora and a perfect environment for pathogens to proliferate.

The solution is clean up the soils, remineralize the crops, and the animals will be healthy and their feed conversion will be

maximized as it is supposed to be. Animals get sick because
of their poor nutrition. Feed conversion is poor because the
nutritional value of the feed, poor ration balancing and the
disruption of the animal gut flora by pesticides in the feed,
and animal stress.

A European study looked at antibiotics in the environment
and the risk of human exposure to antibiotic resistant infections as a result. "The antibiotic enrofloxacin, which previous
studies have found in soil fertilized with poultry and cattle
manure, was associated with the highest risk of soil contamination in this study of soils fertilized with cattle and pig manure. Tetracycline antibiotics, tylosin and sulfodiazine were
also high risk. . . . "[8]

Antibiotics are a vital pharmaceutical tool in today's society
for the treatment of human and animal infections. More and
more we are experiencing resistant infections in hospitals,
nursing homes, local medical clinics and the grocery stores.
The widespread use of antibiotics in animal feed, NOT to
treat infections, rather to cause leaky gut for improved feed
utilization, is a direct cause of these resistant infections. Consumers need to vote with their dollars at the grocery stores

refusing to buy meat, milk, and egg products from animals fed antibiotics.

Demand labeling of foods containing anything GMO, genetically modified. Buy organic when appropriate. Buy grass-fed and antibiotic-free. This is particularly important for those people on low-glycemic diets eating significant quantities of protein, either vegetable or animal. If these proteins are tainted with pro-inflammatory genetic materials, drugs, pesticides, and saturated fats (yes, I know we need saturated fats, just not those from grain-fed animals), then the consumer will eventually suffer the consequences of these contaminants regardless of the glycemic index or load of the diet.

Glyphosate and atrazine are proven testosterone suppressors, gentlemen. Add them to a little estradiol benzoate in that meat and your wonderful low-glycemic diet will still contribute to fat deposition, "man-boobs," and ED.

Patients and consumers will occasionally claim that they cannot afford "organic" produce so they are forced to buy the more "economical" conventionally grown foods. There are two issues regarding this contention. First of all, unfortunately there is a lot of organic produce on the market that is low brix and pretty sorry looking and tasting, I agree. This is remedied by the consumer demanding high-brix produce and NOT buying the low-brix products. In so doing we can attract produce to the market with better and better nutritional values. Those farmers that just don't "get it" and cannot produce the quality food we need and demand will go out of business and those that "get it" and do produce the desired quality, will prosper and expand.

Second, is the fact that food is our REAL medicine, or at least should be our medicine. As such, it is supposed to provide us with nutrition and sustenance to be healthy. The poorer quality the food we consume the more health problems we encounter and; therefore, the more medical bills/costs we shall have, the lower will be our work performance, and the poorer will be our quality of life. So it is said, "Pay me now or pay me later, but inevitably you will pay."

---

1   Gadberry, Shane. "Growth Implants for Sucklingand Growing Beef Cattle." University of Arkansas Cooperative Extension Service, FSA3019 http://www.uaex.edu/Other_Areas/publications/PDF/FSA-3019.pdf

2   rBGH / rBST. Center for Food Safety.
     http://www.centerforfoodsafety.org/campaign/food-safety/rbgh-
     hormones/rbgh-rbst/

3   Philpott, Tom. "Some Arsenic With That Supermarket Chicken?"
     Mother Jones. Saturday June 11, 2011.
     http://www.motherjones.com/tom-philpott/2011/06/arsenic-chicken-
     fda-roxarsone-pfizer

4   Ofosu, W.I., et al. "Formulation of Annato Feed concentrate for lay-
     ers and the evaluation of egg yolk color preference of consumers."
     Journal of Food Biochemistry.Volume 34, Issue 1, pages 66–77, Feb-
     ruary 2010.
     http://onlinelibrary.wiley.com/doi/10.1111/j.1745-
     4514.2009.00264.x/abstract

5   Statement by Thomas R. Frieden M.D., M.P.H. Director, Centers for
     Disease Control and Prevention, U.S. Department of Health and Hu-
     man Services (HHS) on Antibiotic Resistance and the Threat to Pub-
     lic Health before Committee on Energy and Commerce, Subcommit-
     tee on Health, United States House of Representatives, Wednesday
     April 28, 2010.
     http://www.hhs.gov/asl/testify/2010/04/t20100428b.html

6   http://www.theatlantic.com/health/archive/2011/09/antibiotic-
     resistance-and-the-case-for-organic-poultry-and-meat/245067/ Anti-
     biotic Resistance and the Case for Organic Poultry and Meat. Sep 14
     2011

7   "Is your meat safe?" Frontline. PBS.
     http://www.pbs.org/wgbh/pages/frontline/shows/meat/safe/overview.
     html

8   De La Torre, A. Iglesias, I., Carballo, M., Ramírez, P., Muñoz, M.J.
     (2012). An approach for mapping the vulnerability of European Un-
     ion Soils to Antibiotic Contamination. Science of the Total Environ-
     ment. 414: 672-679.
     http://ec.europa.eu/environment/integration/research/newsalert/pdf/27
     9na4.pdf

Chapter 15
Environmental Consequences and Sustainability

There are many problematic issues regarding our food chain and environment. We are truly faced with a Food Plague in my opinion. Like every plague encountered in the past, we can get through this one, but unlike the plagues of the past, this plague is ubiquitous, deliberately imposed upon society, universal in its disruption of the ebb and flow of natural biological cycles, persistent, and most importantly it is denied, politicized, and psychologically addictive.

As with all biological issues or problems, Nature ultimately provides the solution to such problems if only we recognize and heed the true science that is revealed. Yes, even regarding chemical weapon deployment and genetically engineering of "foods," Nature has the resolution of these problems. Most importantly specific to this "plague," the plague of glyphosate and GMO crops, we must first look at what must be done to prevent or eliminate the reasoning behind the propaganda perpetuating the use and spread of glyphosate and genetically engineered crops.

Weeds, crop diseases, and insect pests are proposed "villains" in this regard allegedly robbing the grower and the consumer of vital food and fiber resources; resources vital to the very survival of humankind. A noble and honorable quest receiving little justified recognition is often the complaint coming from growers and agricultural PR outlets. So noble, it is contended, that poisons developed by military chemical weapons' scientists must not be labeled as such, rather they are labeled "crop protection products" to convey the "truer benevolence" of their use.

The chemical weapons industry want the public to believe that, "It matters not that "crop protection products" are truly chemical weapons proven to cause cancer, birth defects, metabolic chaos and death because the end (crop production for humankind) justifies the means. It matters not that a percentage of the population suffers and dies, the greater good must be considered."

Truly "belief" is all that exists with this industry because there is NO SCIENCE in this argument, in this operating model. It is pure "spin," entirely the perpetuation of fiction, falsehood, a lie.

We start first with weeds. Oh, those dastardly plants disrupting our beautiful grass lawns, athletic fields, driveways, and golf courses. You know to what I am referring, those dandelions, thistles, and pigweeds. They are the same weeds that can take over a field of corn, soybeans, broccoli, grapes, blueberries, or apples. If the soil is fertile for growing our food, it is perfect for growing those dastardly weeds as well, everyone knows that don't they?

Just like everyone knew that the earth was flat, illness was due to evil spirits, supersonic flight or man's flight at all was impossible, Neil Armstrong would disappear in a mound of dust upon taking his first step onto the moon, Elvis is still alive, and the genome project would lead to genetic cures for all diseases. I realize that there are still people who believe all these myths to be true.

Every plant has a specific characteristic, a specific uniqueness in reference to its nutritional makeup, its phytonutrient complexity and most importantly, it's "microflora symbiotica." Research done in Scandinavia showed that the successional appearance of different plants starting with bacteria on raw lava rock on through to mature forests is driven by and truly determined by the microflora occupying the rock or soil, colonizing the roots of the plants in question.

Work by Dr. Elaine Ingham further confirmed the Scandinavian research. Plant eco-systems begin with bacteria on rock. As "time" moves on, more diversity in bacteria occurs and then primitive fungi show up.

Lichens and primitive plants (termed today as weeds) come into the area and once the biomass of microbes in the soil reaches a 50/50 split between bacteria and fungi, the fungi dependent plants begin to dominate, including fescue, our current food crops other than brasicas.

Eventually trees dominate the soil landscape when the fungi to bacteria ratio gets greatly in favor of the fungi perhaps 100 or even 1000 to 1 biomass relationship. It is so important for the reader to understand that this is the course of plant life progression and survival in the natural world, free of herbicides, insecticides, fungicides, and miticides.

How is it possible that the vast forests of 200 years ago could have survived without man-made chemical weapons? That same question could be asked of the great prairie grasslands? How is it possible that "weeds" didn't choke out these lush, nutritious grasslands of the Midwest and western U.S.?

It is very simple really, nutrition! The soils of the vast grasslands and forests were fungal dominated, beneficial fungi, that is, mycorrhizal fungi for the most part. Symbiotic with these beneficial fungi were many beneficial bacteria both colonizing the roots of these grasses and trees protecting them from disease organisms and nourishing them for good health and longevity.

Most important here is for the reader to understand that the reason your lawn, athletic field, driveway, golf course, pasture, or crop field is full of weeds is because you have set up the soil perfect for the weeds to grow. You have neglected to realize that your grass and crops require and higher successional microbial balance to be healthy. Nature is working to balance the soil though Nature's timetable may be 1,000 years. With proper understanding and more importantly, appropriate fertilization and management, the weeds can be made to "disappear" and your desired grass or crop be made more healthy and vigorous.

I fully realize that if you ask your county extension agent, the local co-op fertilizer dealer, the resident golf course superintendent, and many farmers, they will all tell you that "it just ain't so." They are correct, "it ain't so' for them. They don't understand and haven't a clue how to properly fertilize and manage the soil. They only know what the chemical weapons industry have taught them. People every day in our lives tell us we cannot do things; things that they cannot do such as play professional sports, become an astronaut, go to vet school, run a marathon, cure cancer, farm without chemical weapons, and out-yield those who do farm with chemical weapons. Even when shown on their own farms or university test plots, there are those "sticks in the mud" that will continue to deny that we can farm successfully without the use of chemical weapons and out yield current record yields.

Many of those "naysayers" are of course heavily invested or vested in the chemical and biotech industry so pay out on their financial investments depends upon the perpetuation of chemical weapons and genetically engineered plants. Many of them mouth the mantra that we would all starve to death without these chemical weapons (crop protection products). The reality is that the western world is starving to death on full stomachs.

On the practical side, we will have to do something in the transition period to address weeds. Some farmers will learn to use herbicides more judiciously in conjunction with physical soil management techniques such as cultivation, shading and timing of events. Gone is the scorched earth approach. There are a few "organic" weed control products on the market but these are fairly pricy and are more "burn down" materials that include 200 grain vinegar, sulfur, pine extract, or the like. Key is getting the fertilization right. In some cases we can get good weed suppression with a timely spray of liquid calcium over the top of the soil.

A very effective method is to plant a green manure or cover crop as part of the crop rotation. (Green manure refers to the planting of a mixed plant cover such as vetch, clover, oats, peas, etc., feeding it to maximize its brix level and the reincorporating it back into the soil.) Combined with appropriate fertilization and microbial inoculation, this management process moves the soil's successional status toward more mature fungal domination, which is less conducive to weed growth. Don't be misled by farmers that contend they cannot do this because it is too expensive. Rotating a green manure crop into the cropping cycle actually increases yield of the subsequent years, conserves soil moisture, reduces weeds, diseases, and insects.

The chemical weapons industry had convinced farmers that the best way to get the green manure crop incorporated back into the soil is to spray it with glyphosate to kill it and then no-till plant into the dead residue. This practice completely defeats the point and purpose of green manure rotation into the cropping cycle. As mentioned earlier, the glyphosate is translocated to the roots and excreted into the soil killing beneficial soil microflora, inducing the increase in soil pathogens (of course that is great for selling more soil fungicides), tying up vital soil micronutrients. This process results in the crop residue oxidizing back into the air as carbon dioxide. It merely perpetuates the scorched earth approach.

Next is the crop disease issue. Fungal, bacterial, and viral diseases are a real problem for crop production around the world, and like weed infestation, are increasing with increased use of pesticides. Resistance to chemical weapons is common. The common mentality is that diseases and insect pests are due entirely because of a chemical weapons deficiency. Yes, chemical weapons DEFICIENCY! I know, how ridiculous, but that is the mentality perpetuated by farmers, extension agents, and, of course, the chemical weapons industry. Diseases and insect pests only infect sick plants. It is their job to recycle inferior plants, plants that do not provide mammals with the nutrition necessary to be healthy.

Ask yourself how we survived before the 20th century, how did people grow crops in ancient Middle East without pesticides? How did Asia grow rice without pesticides? Nutrition is the answer and chemical weapons disrupt or outright inhibit appropriate nutritional flow to the plant perpetuating further disease, insect pressure and weed growth. It is a great business plan for perpetually selling more chemical weapons.

Remember back to the discussion on glyphosate. Glyphosate chelates, ties up trace elements especially manganese, copper, zinc, cobalt and selenium. In doing so it disrupts vital metabolic life cycles in plants and microbes. August 10, 2010, it was patented as an antibiotic so all the lip service coming out of the chemical weapons industry, extension services, and farmers to the contrary, glyphosate kills beneficial soil microbes, most notably pseudomonas genera.

Pseudomonas directly inhibits fusarium pathogenic fungi that cause many common plant diseases such as "Sudden Death" in soybeans and produce toxic mycotoxins in grains. Get the nutrient levels, brix levels, of the crop up to the "excellent" range and these plants will simply be free of disease.

The same holds true for insect infestation. Insect pests are truly nature's garbage collectors intended to recycle the garbage not fit for human consumption. As Chaboussau (French biologist) and Callahan (American entomologist) proved decades ago, insects attach only sick plants. Their digestive systems are different than that of mammals (novel concept) and, therefore, they cannot eat what is truly healthy and intended for fulfilling the nutrient needs of mammals.

Understand that when plants truly have sufficient nutrition, (high brix) they consist of and produce complete, complex carbohydrates and proteins, all not digestible by insect pests. When these same plants are deficient in nutrients (low brix), they cannot complete the manufacturing of complex carbohydrates and proteins; therefore, they contain many free amino acids, free nitrogenous compounds, simple and free sugars, all very digestible and desirable for insect pests.

Fundamentally the difference between insect food and mammalian food is nutrition and the complexity of the carbohydrates and proteins. When farmers kill the garbage collectors and supply the "garbage" to mammals, mammals get sick, weak, and diseased. This conveniently leads to more sales of yet more chemical weapons cleverly packages as pharmaceuticals. It is a great business plan. Mind you, as a physician I prescribe drugs in my practice. I have to in order to address the acute illnesses, but I also work to address the underlying cause of these diseases: poor soil fertility.

Chapter 16

Organic versus Not Organic

This hot topic garners heated debate around the world, fervent opinionated rhetoric, and most importantly much disappointment at the supermarket. People cannot get much nutrition from philosophy. It is real hard to savor the flavor of something that tastes like cardboard or is half rotten before you can get it onto your dinner plate. Organic, specifically "certified organic," fruits and vegetables demand a premium price in most grocery stores yet present the quintessential paradox for the consumer.

Some of the absolutely best, most nutrient dense, most mouth-watering, flavorful, and longest lasting fruits and vegetables on the market are "certified organically" grown. At the same time some of the absolutely worst, least nutrient dense, least flavorful, and fastest rotting fruits and vegetables on the market are "certified organically" grown.

How is this possible to have such a dichotomy, extreme opposites, yet both being "certified organically" grown? Very simple: Organic certification is a procedural and philosophically driven certification approach, NOT an outcome driven approach. The assumption philosophy, and it is just philosophy, is that following the prescribed procedure of only using, if you use anything at all, approved inputs/fertilizers/soil amendments on the farm automatically produces the desired outcome: better quality fruits and vegetables.

Have you ever heard an organic farmer or advocate say that the organic product is better because there were no pesticides, harsh chemicals, or hormones used to produce the product? It was done the way "Nature intended it to be done"? Yes, repeatedly I have heard these statements. That's all procedural and if it's junk, Nature sends in the garbage crew, insects, to remove it from the food chain. That's the way Nature intends it to be!

The real problem is that there is no real concrete outcome standard. There is no real understanding that the sole purpose for the food crop is to provide NUTRITIONAL SUSTENANCE to the consumer. Both the organic and non-organic farmers suffer this lack of understanding. There is no real understanding that the most important aspect of any food is the nutritional value gained by the consumer upon consumption of the food; what vitamins, minerals, amino acids, enzymes, fatty acids, and phytonutrients are gained from eating the produce by the consumer.

As was already discussed, the sap or juice brix level correlates well with the nutritional value of any fruit or vegetable at harvest. Low-brix produce is low in nutrient whether it is "certified organic" or not.

The contention by organic farmers is that they don't use synthetic pesticides so their product is better. Let's examine that perspective for a moment. If the crop nutrition is poor, the crop sap brix is poor, then, as pointed out previously, insects and disease will attack. Rather than using synthetic pesticides, the organic farmer uses elemental sulfur, copper sulfate, pyrethrum, Bt, neem and karanja oil, garlic oil, predator insects, and hand removal.

The weaker the crop, the lesser toxic pest control materials, such as predator insects, garlic, neem and karanja oil and even Bt are inadequate, therefore, the more sulfur and copper sulfate the farmers use. Again, the discussion is really about nutrition, not genetics. The better the crop nutrition, the stronger will be the plant. The stronger the plant, the more complex the fats, proteins, and carbohydrates, the more plant secondary compounds will be produced; subsequently, the fewer will be the diseases and insect pests.

There are a few areas in Australia where "organic farmers" had to be banned from using copper sulfate because they polluted the ground water with it. Pyrethroids have been proven to be quite toxic to humans and animals. Another study showed that though "organic" produce contained no residues of currently used pesticides; they did contain the same and in some cases higher levels of old and often banned pesticide such as DDT because they were grown on soils that 30 or more years ago had these pesticides applied to them.

> "Synthetic pyrethroids have largely replaced organophosphates in some arenas especially domestic home use. Recent research finds these chemicals to be endocrine disrupting, as rat studies show the inhibition of estrogen in young females, delaying puberty, bone and tissue development."

http://www.ehponline.org/members/2008/11119/11
119.html

The point here is that the discussion debating whether "organic produce" is better than "non-organic" produce because of the difference in what pesticides were used is senseless and pure political rhetoric. The simple fact that any pesticide, whether "approved organic" or synthetic, needed to be used to protect the crop from nature's garbage crew means that the crop was grown with less nutrition than it needed. It means that the brix levels are lower than they should be; it means that the nutritional value to the consumer is less than needed for the consumer to be healthy and satisfied physiologically. This debate is like saying that you used a knife or hammer to kill the invader rather than a gun so you are more justified in your action.

Certainly there is a transitional time in taking a soil from degenerated to that minimal level of fertility where it will produce high-brix crops and during this time we may need to use "pesticides' of some type just to get a crop. Any crop is better than no crop, of course, but each year of appropriate soil and plant nutritional management, the need for such a "pesticide" will decrease as the crop nutrient value increases.

This is the concept the consumer needs to understand, needs to demand at the grocery story; high-brix fruits and vegetables. Yes, it would be great if they were "organic" but if you have the choice between a 13 brix "organic apple" and an 18 brix "non-organic" apple, both fresh off the tree at those values, both the same variety, then the 18 brix apple will be better for you and most often be lower in chemical residue. Yes, I know the organics supposedly didn't use pesticides so how could the organic apple possible have more pesticide residue than the non-organic apple. Simple, old residual pesticides such as DDT/DDE in the soil (applied decades ago) are still taken up by organically grown crops. The nutrient balance of the tree determines what and how much of what will be taken up with respect to pesticides, by the tree. Bottom line, eat the higher brix apple and demand the organic farmer improve his crop nutrition.

We live in a world where the pesticides are readily found in the wind and rain water, as well as irrigation and drainage water. Anyone who thinks there is such a thing as true organic is fooling themselves. Pesticide residue is not just a factor of what and how much was applied to the crop, but also a factor of the quality of the crop, the crop nutritional health for as that increases the crop takes up less of the chemicals to which it is exposed whether directly/deliberately or via drift and rain.

Now that I have said all this, I buy organic whenever I can find quality "organic" because first and foremost at present, I must avoid genetically engineered foods. GMOs are not currently allowed in organic systems. Second, there are a growing number of "organic farmers" around the country that really understand these concepts and are truly getting the nutrition into their crops combining the best of agricultural science and the safety of organic farming practices.

I seek out those organic farmers that are producing the absolute best produce and then market what I described at the beginning of this section. This is what I seek whenever possible. Unfortunately is it still too few and far between, but continued consumer demand at the grocery store is increasing the opportunity for finding truly healthful fruits and vegetables.

This brings up the price debate. Everyone likes getting a deal. Everyone likes feeling like they made a good purchase and got what or more than what they paid. At the same time, none of us likes feeling like we got taken or were over charged. The complaint that "organic" foods cost too much is really a complaint that the consumer doesn't really feel he or she is getting his/her money's worth for what they had to pay. If the produce costs $1 per pound or $10 per pound, truly the actual price is not really the issue.

If you spend $1 per pound on lettuce and throw half to two-thirds in the trash before you get to eat it and what you did eat you had to smother with dressing to tolerate the bitter taste, you paid too much. On the other hand if you paid $10 per pound for the lettuce and it lasted for a week with no spoilage and you needed little if any dressing because it was so sweet and tasty and all your dinner guests raved about how good the salad tasted, you got a great deal.

Further, if the $1 per pound lettuce causes stomach upset, gas, reflux, and you were hungry five minutes after eating, that $1 per pound lettuce was too expensive a purchase. If the nutritional value is present in the product, you will feel better and be healthier spending less on additional foods, garnishments, sweets, poor health, and medical bills. The same goes for meat, eggs, and milk.

One way or another, you will be paying out the money, either for the food or for the lost health and medical bills. Where do you prefer to spend your money? The cost must be tied to actual value, not rhetoric or procedure. If the "organic" looks poor, smells poorly, tastes bland, and rots, it is too expensive at any price. Food, "organic" or otherwise is expensive if it contributes to chronic disease (low-brix, low mineral, poor shelf life, poor looks) and cheap if it contributes to health (high brix, high mineral, great shelf life, great looks), regardless of the initial cost.

Chapter 17

Grass-fed versus Grain-fed

There is an entire movement afoot called the grass-fed movement. You can find much about this from the teaching of Joel Salatin, a delightful gentleman who has figured out how to raise most everything on grass, from beef to chickens, pigs to ducks. His teachings and the teachings of others along a similar vane, garner nice touchy-feely thoughts of a simpler lifestyle, getting back to nature and wholesome food production. That is all very nice, but what really is at issue here? Is this just a philosophical debate, one in which the "green revolution" pundits contend they can win as soon as one talks serious food production for an ever expanding world population? That is certainly what the "agricultural-industrial complex" would like us all to believe.

This is, as are all these issues, truly a discussion about food quality, specifically the nutritional value of the fatty acids and fats of the food consumed. Most importantly in this discussion is the concept that ruminant animals, cattle, sheep, goats, and deer, are designed to eat grass. Technically sheep, goats, and deer are not just grazers but also browsers, meaning they will eat shrubs, tree leaves, lichens, etc. They are total herbivores.

Basic nutrition for the production of meat and milk requires energy and protein, plus many other nutrients as well, but fundamentally energy and protein. Both should and can be obtained from grass for the grazers. Actually "grass" should be mixed species of grasses and plants making up any pasture so the grazing animal gets a variety of plants to consume. The problem is that farmers have neglected the nutritional requirement of the soil necessary to produce high-brix grass for the animals to eat. High-brix grass will be high in energy and protein, true complex carbohydrate and complex protein. Modern farming practice in all its infinite ignorance had decided to feed ruminants grain because it is a concentrated energy source and bean meals (soybean, linseed, cottonseed) or urea to supply added protein to the animal diet all because available grass and/or forages are low brix and low protein.

As a side note, there are many ranchers and grazing farms that do little or no fertilization of their pasture or grazing ranges, and have not for decades or centuries. What they have done is treat the animals with anti-parasitic drugs, such as Ivomectin, which pass out in the manure, thus, contaminating the soil, reducing soil beneficial biology resulting in reduced fertility, increased erosion, and further decrease in pasture nutrient value. They have and continue to "mine" the soil.

Understand that the ruminant digestive system is primarily an acetic acid (vinegar) driven system, at least a grass-fed ruminant digestive system is primarily an acetic acid driven system. Acetic acid in the digestive system becomes the precursor for CLA and the omega-3 fatty acids in the meat and milk of the animal, a healthy animal.

When grain is fed as the primary energy supply, the rumen converts from an acetic acid driven system to a propionic acid driven system. This is because the grain significantly alters the rumen microflora. Propionic acid is pro-inflammatory to the animal and is the precursor to arachidonic acid and saturated fat in the meat and milk. With the rumen flora significantly altered, pathogenic microbes begin to evolve and become problematic.

The addition of bean meal and/or urea further alters the rumen microflora, which leads to more inflammation, premature aging, and higher ammonia and nitrogen content in the milk and meat. All this inflammation begets fluid retention, which of course means weight gain, perfect for the farmer selling strictly by the pound.

If one merely tours a slaughterhouse, he or she will observe the inflamed digestive systems and diseased/condemned livers from these animals. So, in a nutshell, grain is fed for energy because the animal is not getting enough energy from the typical grass or forage. The grass or forage is low in energy because of inadequate farm management that produces grass or forage with low brix.

Most farmers don't understand how to improve the forage brix/nutrient density so they opt for the grain. Grain is also more fun to grow and harvest than is pasture because bigger toys (tractors, tillage/planting equipment and harvest equipment) can be used. It is a classic "boys and their toys" situation. Additionally, the government promotes the grain program because it leads to more tax revenue from all the equipment manufacturing and sales, transportation revenue and veterinary drug sales revenue.

The bottom line is that with appropriate soil management, the farmer can produce high-brix grass forage, high in both energy and protein that results in profitable/competitive weight gains and milk production from the animals with healthy fats in both the meat and milk at less cost per pound of meat and milk production than with the standard "green revolution" model perpetuated today by the ag-industrial complex. High-brix pasture will produce more meat and milk per acre of land used than will the conventional feedlot system and do so without all the environmental destruction, food contamination, pesticide/petrochemical poisoning; meat and milk that are more nutritious and healthful for the consumer in an truly sustainable manner.

Grass-fed beef and milk are truly better for the consumer if only considering the issue of saturated fats in the diet. Grass-fed are lower in saturated fats and higher in the omega-3, polyunsaturated fats, and CLA, conjugated linoleic acid. There are many people that have significant digestive problems with grain-fed beef but no digestive problems with grass-fed beef.

Another issue near and dear to many is the worldwide desertification of arable land. All these lands can be reclaimed appropriate grazing programs. Allan Savory, world renowned biologist, gives a delightful presentation for TED: "Allan Savory: How to green the world's deserts and reverse climate change."
http://www.youtube.com/watch?v=vpTHi7O66pI&feature=youtu.be&inf_contact_key=6381d833dccab6f55e694b425ae9614dc80fba5b06912a5946448c9c418cbdbf

He has a follow up question and answer session, "Allan Savory: Q&A Session—Reversing Global Warming while Meeting Human Needs: An Urgently Needed Land-Based Option Q&A Session." Allan Savory, President & Cofounder, The Savory Institute. Friedman School of Nutrition Science and Policy, Tufts University.
http://www.youtube.com/watch?v=QxPNPXbVtfI

Possible sources of information include:
www.americangrassfed.org, www.uswellnessmeats.com, www.northamericandevon.com, www.americandevon.com.

Chapter 18

Wild versus Farm-raised Fish

There are perhaps several political or philosophical viewpoints to discuss regarding fish, fishing and our fishing reserves, but I will leave that for another discussion. The focus of this discussion is the quality of the food. Wild fish has many nutritional benefits including very healthful protein, a great variety of minerals, including vital iodine and omega-3 fatty acids. Certainly the theory behind farm-raised fish is to reduce the pressure on wild fish resources while supplying an ever increasing demand for fish and seafood in general. Fundamental to all living food sources is that each is a reflection, a result of the diet which it is fed.

Wild fish are uniquely nutritious for us to eat because of their wild diet. It is the diet that affords them the protein, minerals and omega-3 fats. Farm raised fish are fed more like commercial pigs and chickens than fish in the wild. Consequently, farmed raise fish are being fed grains, particularly today genetically engineered grains, bean meal especially genetically engineered soybean and cottonseed meal resulting in fish higher in saturated fats, lower in omega-3 fats and very concerning, many times higher in PCBs.

All the hype about mercury in fish is literally dwarfed by the level of PCBs in farmed raised fish. It is another testament to the complete lack of consideration for the value of the food product being produced by the farmer focusing only on volume of a commodity and the personal profit to be had in the short term.

The next great threat to both our fish resources and out own personal health is the introduction of genetically engineered fish. Like their counterpart genetically engineered crops, GE fish are foreign proteins and a threat to our immune system, to our health and longevity.

The probable consequence of feeding fish grain, particularly genetically engineered grain is the compromise of their immune system. Consequent to this immune compromise is the infection of farm-raised fish with various sea lice, parasites and viruses. This reality is manifesting in British Columbia Salmon, both farmed and wild. Several viruses originating in the cage fish farms anchored at the mouths of major rivers in British Columbia including the Frazer River are killing fish. These viruses proliferate, mutate and contaminate the environment via fish farms. Examples include ISA—Infectious Salmon Anemia, Salmon Alphavirus and Piscine Reovirus. I suggest viewing the documentary video: http://vimeo.com/61301410# "Salmon Confidential—How a Canadian Government Cover-Up Threatens Your Health, and the Entire Ecosystem."

Chapter 19

A1 v. A2 Milk

World milk production is estimated to be about 668 million metric ton, India being the largest producer at 102 million metric tons with the U.S. second at 86 million metric tons. Over half of the world milk production is produced under the "American model" of commercialized, feed lot focused management and breed selection. That means that over half of the world milk production, nearly 100 percent of the Western world, produces A1 milk.[1]

What does "A1 milk" mean and what is the significance?

Milk consists of different proteins. One dominant protein is casein. There are two different casein proteins depending upon the breed and ancestry of the cow producing the milk. The difference between the two proteins rests at amino acid position 67 in the protein molecule of casein. A1 casein contains a histidine amino acid at position 67 while A2 casein contains a proline amino acid. The difference is significant regarding the biochemical change that occurs when this milk protein is heated and/or digested and then the subsequent physiological response of the consumer. When A1 milk is heated or digested, the casein molecule breaks at position 67 because the histidine amino acid is more weakly bound, thus, liberating beta-casomorphine-7(BCM7), an opiate.

A2 milk's casein protein molecule, containing the amino acid proline at position 67, does not break with heating or digestion and, thus, does not form/release BCM7. There is an interesting trail of intrigue associated with this difference. It is estimated that about 5000 years ago a mutation occurred in the dairy cattle causing the histidine amino acid replacement of proline in certain cattle. Interestingly, A1 cattle seem to lend themselves better to feedlot life while A2 cattle, being the original bovine milk producer, lend themselves better to grazing life. The Holstein cow is A1 and perpetuated throughout "Americanized" dairy around the world.

Why is this important in our discussion of food quality and health? Fonterra, the largest dairy coop in the world, based in New Zealand, in the 1970's funded research into the differences between A1 and A2 milk thinking there might be some sort of marketing advantage for them to do so since, at that time nearly all the milk cows in New Zealand were A2 cows and Fonterra was marketing New Zealand milk around the world competing against A1 milk from the U.S. and Europe. What Fonterra researchers found was so profound and revolutionary, that the company did everything it could to subsequently suppress their own research findings for fear it would destroy the dairy industry as it was presently operating.

The research showed that the BCM7 peptide from A1 milk had a stronger correlation to heart disease than did cigarette smoking; that it had a direct correlation in the cause of type I diabetes with more recent research showing a correlation with autism and schizophrenia. Let me repeat, the dominant milk sold in the industrialized world (except France), A1, Holstein, has a stronger correlation to heart disease than does cigarette smoking. In the U.S., cigarette companies are no longer allowed to advertise on TV and buyers must be 18 to purchase them. Heart disease is the number one killer in the Western world. The American dairy industry has so infiltrated the U.S. government that milk, yes A1 milk correlated more strongly than cigarette smoking with causing heart disease, is promoted in school lunch programs as a MUST for every child in America.

BCM7 is an opiate, which is addictive; as are cigarettes. Interesting work on the BCM7 peptide was initially done at Children's Hospital in Kansas City, Missouri by Dr. Bill Shaw as director of the medical laboratory. Dr. Shaw, doing organic and amino acid analyses of urines from autistic children, noticed a peculiar frequency band in all these children's urine. He eventually identified it a BCM7 and further research found this opiate to be highly correlative to aberrant behavior in these children. When parents would take children off milk, they would experience withdrawal symptoms as if they were taken off prescription or recreational opiate drugs.

A2 milk, produced by the older Jerseys, Asian, and African cows, not producing BCM7, is not addictive and is not correlated with increasing heart disease, diabetes, autism or schizophrenia. These cattle are grazers, they eat grass, which as already discussed, leads to higher beneficial and lower saturated fats in the milk and meat. This issue runs deep in the dairy industry. Associated with feedlot dairying is the milking parlor industry, the corn grain and silage industries, the fertilizer and pesticide industries, the equipment manufacturing industries, the cattle breeding industries, the veterinarian and drug industries and then of course the profitable heart disease treatment industry. All have strong vested interest in perpetuating A1 milk.

Fortunately, there are people with integrity, companies with leaders who have integrity. One of those is Organic Valley, a La Farge, Wisconsin, dairy cooperative. Thanks to Dr. Paul Dettloff, their consulting organic veterinarian and their leadership, they require all their producers to be at least 60 percent grass-fed, are teaching them to increase the brix of the pastures and are teaching their producers to purchase only A2 genetics.

There will always be consumers that will complain about the price of everything. The reality is that one gets that for which one pays. You may think you are saving on the grocery bill by buying the cheaper A1 milk. You will pay in behavior problems, heart disease and diabetes. The behavior problems will be immediate as over 30 percent of American children are now medicated for ADHD. The heart and diabetes problems will be delayed payments, but payments nonetheless.

There is a book called *The Devil in the Milk*, written by agri-business professor and farm-management consultant Keith Woodford. In this book Dr. Woodford lays out the theory that there is a devil in some of our milk, and this is something we need to come to grips with.

There are some very intriguing anecdotal stories about the use of A2 raw milk for the successful calming of Crohn's disease in patients where nothing else is helping including steroids. It is indeed a thought provoking concept, one that needs further pursuit.

---

1   Beldman, Alfons. "Trends and challenges in world dairy farming Impressions from the 2009 Global Dairy Farmers congress in China."March 2010, The Hague.
     http://www.lei.dlo.nl/publicaties/PDF/2010/2010-015.pdf

Chapter 20

Pesticides and endocrine disruptors

We have already discussed the existence of glyphosate residues in food products. It is not the only farm chemical found in the food. All these chemicals, for the most part, are endocrine disruptors meaning they interfere with proper function of hormones in one's body from thyroid to acetylcholine, insulin cortisol, pregnenolone to estrogen and testosterone. The World Health Organization (WHO) definition of an endocrine disruptor that the European Union (EU) adopted in 1999 is:

> " An endocrine disruptor is an exogenous substance or mixture that alters function(s) of the endocrine system and consequently causes adverse health effects in an intact organism or its progeny or subpopulations."

These chemicals are in the food because they are sprayed on the soil that grow the food and sprayed directly on the food itself. Industry soft peddles these chemical poisons as "crop protection agents" wanting to convince the consumer that they are benevolent saviors of human food stores and business enterprises against the "evil ravages" of nature's predators. How comforting, NOT. They are poisons, chemical weapons designed to kill cells by nutrient chelation and endocrine disruption. Many of these weapon pundits will espouse that such poisons improve the quality of our food. How does that work, one should ask? A poison improves my food quality?

What nutrient, mineral, vitamin, amino acid, fatty acid, antioxidant, phytonutrient do these poisons add to my food? As stated before, if they truly improve the quality of our food then we should all have an additional product shaker on our tables in addition to the salt and pepper shakers. We should have a shaker for these chemical poisons so that we can be sure to add these chemicals to our food at the table ensuring we "maximize" the quality of that food we are about to consume. Antonio Molina-Diaz, et al., found,

 ""(R)elatively large' concentrations of pesticides, measured in micrograms per litre, were found in a number of the subject extracts. Pesticides, such as carbendazim, thiabendazole, imazalil and malathion, which are applied to crops after harvesting and can remain on fruits and vegetables, were found in finished products during the study, stated the researchers."[1]

Pesticides, nearly by definition, are endocrine disruptors. Endocrine disruption is associated with thyroid dysfunction and disease, adrenal exhaustion and chronic fatigue. It is associated with estrogen and progesterone disruption in women and low testosterone, high estrogen in men. Endocrine disruption is associated with precocious puberty, infertility and cancer in both men and women. It is associated with insulin disruption, diabetes and pancreatic cancer. It is associated with neurotransmitter disruption and behavior problems.

Pesticides are nearly ubiquitous in our environment and food today. Most importantly, understand that pesticides are chelators of minerals. That is their mechanism of action. They disrupt hormonal or metabolic pathways by chelating or stealing the trace mineral co-factors of these vital enzymes, hormones or peptides. In so doing, the enzyme of hormone function is altered or stopped. Chronically, this is means a slow "bleed" of vital nutrients from one's body coupled with the decline in nutrients obtained from one's diet; thus, disease manifests.

Each person will be a bit different in their timing and response because of individual diet and because of generational
susceptibility as families tend to eat similarly.

It is all about inertia. The stronger one's nutrient reserve, the
greater will be one's metabolic inertia to maintain health. The
lower one's nutritional reserve or inertia, the more susceptible
one will be to all the assaults of life, chemical toxins and pesticides. Think about the difference between a bicycle and a
train. It takes little energy to start a bicycle moving and I is
easily blown off track, diverted and stopped.

The train engine, on the other hand, takes a lot of energy to
get moving and once it is moving it takes a lot of energy to
change its course or stop it. Though the bicycle can go just as
fast as the train and actually reach peak speed more quickly,
there is significant difference in the inertia between the two.
So it is with nutrient reserve/inertia in the human body. Pesticides are significant diverters of metabolic function. The less
nutrient inertia a body possesses, the more readily the pesticide will alter body metabolic function. Further, as already
discussed, there are generational considerations as an expo-

sure to one generation does readily affect subsequent genera-tions even if those generations don't have exposure.

An example of this inertia is with the following studies on Parkinson's and exposure to organophosphate pesticides as-sociated with Gulf War I. Every soldier did not get Parkin-son's, but the incidence in soldiers returning from the Gulf was far above the population average. One may wonder why all the soldiers didn't come back with Parkinson's. Under-stand that there were several factors summed together making up what is termed "total load" on the immune and detoxifica-tion systems that precipitated this problem.

These factors include initially the stress of leaving home and going to war; the long flight and time changes to the Gulf; military food/processed food; climate change; a handful of immunizations at one time. All these lead-up stressors ex-haust some of the reserve antioxidants in the body. Add to these stressors exposure to organophosphates sprayed all over the living quarters coupled with the pyrethroids (all uniforms were impregnated with pyrethrum) and then the stress of combat. For some soldiers one can add exposure to DU and biological weapons. (Yes, contrary to media denial, bio weapons were used in Gulf War I).

All these stressors have to be directly or indirectly processed through the liver and dealt with via the detox system. If the individual soldier's nutrient reserve is adequate, the "total load" of stressors does not get the upper hand. If, on the other hand, the "total load" of stressors is greater than the nutrient reserve can tolerate, he or she will manifest some illness response, in this case Parkinson's. Nutritional inertia explains why some solders experience Parkinson's while others did not. Further, as Richard Francis explains in his book, "Epigenetics: How Environment Shapes Our Genes" the environmental and emotional exposure these soldiers experience in the womb and in childhood shaped their susceptibility to stressors later in life.

East Texas Medical Center, Tyler, TX

18-month study; organic pesticides v. Parkinson's

> "people with Parkinson's were 10 times more likely to have been exposed to rotenone."

> Risk is 1:40 nationwide but 1:4 in the Midwest farm belt and in the petroleum industry

Parkinson's sufferers were "twice as likely to have used pesticides with chlorpyrifos, such as Dursban."

http://etmc.org/pesticidestudy.htm

2001 Pesticide Use EPA Data

Herbicides/Plant Growth Regulators 553 (H&G 11%)

Insecticides/Miticides 105 (H & G 12%)

Fungicides 73 (H & G 15%)

Nematicide/Fumigant 127 (H & G 1%)

Other Conventional 30 (H & G3%)

Total 888 million pounds active ingredient (H & G 10%)

"Other Conventional" pesticides include rodenticides, mulluscicides, aquatic and fish/bird pesticides, and other miscellaneous conventional pesticides.

U.S. pesticide amount used in both 2000 and 2001 exceeded 1.2 billion pounds. 73 mil lb. organophosphate

H & G stands for home and garden use.

http://www.epa.gov/opp00001/pestsales/01pestsales/usage2001_2.htm

Most of the toxicology research done on pesticides and chemicals are all based upon single product exposure on a dose-response curve. No consideration is given for small doses over extended periods of time. No consideration is given for real life experience of hundreds to thousands of chemicals and pesticides in combination over extended periods of time. Total load is the key to whether a person experiences an illness or reaction. One's response is all about nutrient reserve or nutrient inertia.

The mantra of the typical toxicologist is "dose-response." This is true of linear environments, but natural environments, the human body, are not linear, they are non-linear environments. Benachour, et al., counter this madness of "the dose makes the toxin" stating:

" . . . (A) negligible amount acting during months or years can be more disordering in a durable way (and even with transgenerational effects) than a short exposure to a high dose. . . . (T)he concept of 'threshold,'S without taking duration into account, is not really scientific."[2]

Toxicologist, Dr. Warren Porter at the University of Wisconsin studying pesticides in our environment and their low dose effect on children found:

Sonora, Mexico, Yaqui Indian preschoolers in farmed valley where groundwater was contaminated with pesticides compared to children in the foothills with "clean" groundwater. Valley 4- and 5-year-olds showed DIFFICULTIES WITH SIMPLE TASKS, HAD POORER MEMORIES AND SHOWED MORE AGGRESSION AND ANGRY OUTBURSTS.

Dr. Porter further reported in the Mid-March 1999 issue of *Toxicology and Industrial Health*:

" . . . Combinations of chemicals can alter thyroid hormones, suppress immune systems and affect nervous functions. . . . " The effects were strongest when a single PESTICIDE OR HERBICIDE WAS COMBINED WITH NITRATE.

Nitrogen is the most widely and excessively used fertilizer in "modern" agriculture demonstrated by the widespread nitrogen pollution of the waterways on every continent in the world. Consequently, low doses of pesticides are commonly combined with nitrate nitrogen in ground, swimming and drinking water. Children are especially vulnerable to such exposures due to their rapid developing bodies and changing endocrine and nervous systems. A study at the University of Washington in Seattle led by Dr. Sarah Waller to investigate possible causes of the two- to four-fold increase in the birth defect gastroschisis (a type of abdominal hernia where the intestines can actually grow outside the belly) in eastern Washington. Her study found a link between maternal exposure to agricultural spraying of atrazine, nitrates, and 2,4-dichlorophenoxyacetic acid and gastroschisis birth defects.[3]

Yet another study by Heeren, Tyler and Mandeya over ten years ago linked maternal exposure to pesticides with birth defects in South Africa.

"A total of 89 case mothers and 178 control mothers was interviewed. Babies with birth defects were seven times more likely to be born to women exposed to chemicals used in gardens and fields compared to no reported exposure (Odds Ratio 7.18, 95% CI 3.99, 13.25); and were almost twice as likely to be born to women who were involved in dipping livestock used to prevent ticks (OR 1.92, 95% CI 1.15, 3.14). They were also 6.5 times more likely to be born to women who were using plastic containers for fetching water (OR 6.5, 95% CI 2.2, 27.9). Some of these containers had previously contained pesticides (OR 1.87, 95% CI 1.06, 3.31)."[4]

There are two questions to be asked regarding these and other examples of pesticide exposures: What can be done to counter the effects of the exposures and how do we prevent the exposures in the first place. The answer to the second question has already been covered: clean up agriculture, implement scientific nutritional farm management technology and practices that raise crop brix readings, and thus, nutrient values. This results in health plants that are not attacked by insect pests and diseases and soils that have more climax biological systems that don't have the week problems so the pesticides are not "needed" in the first place.

The answer to the first question is nutrition. The body's defense systems, particularly its detoxification system is dependent upon a full complement of nutrients, especially antioxidants, to detoxify pesticides and other chemicals with which the body is burdened. The natural outcome of the answer to the second question, proper farm management, results in nutrient dense foods that provide much, most, or all the nutrients and antioxidants necessary for the body to detoxify properly. In the meantime, we must supplement the diet with antioxidants and nutrients to make up for the deficit not supplied by the food.

"Antioxidants are substances that may protect cells from the damage caused by unstable molecules known as free radicals. Free radical damage may lead to cancer. Antioxidants interact with and stabilize free radicals and may prevent some of the damage free radicals otherwise might cause. Examples of antioxidants include beta-carotene, lycopene, vitamins C, E, and A, and other substances."

"The amount of Antioxidants that you maintain in your body is directly related to how long you will live"[5]

Summary: Ladies and gentlemen, the pesticide debate involves a lot of politics; it involves a lot of money. The system of agriculture focusing on nutritional management of the soil and crops is a working system around the world. It is growing by word of mouth and consumer demand for better quality food. It does not make the nightly news because it does not garner expensive Hollywood advertising, star wars fantasy or dot-com style biotech startups. More importantly, it promises to nearly eliminate the lucrative pesticide, drug and biotech seed cash cows so prominent in today's society. It doesn't elicit multi-billion dollar university research funds.

It does, however, solve ALL the problems supposedly addressed by these cash cow industries, while at the same time, regenerating our food system, regenerating our environment, sequestering carbon and eliminating the polluting of our food, environment and people. It works in the real world and that is what counts.[6]

---

1   Molina-Diaz, J. Garcia-Reyes, B. Gilbert-Lopez. "Determination of Pesticide Residues in Fruit-Based Soft Drinks." Analytical Chemistry. Published online, doi: 10.1021/ac8012708 http://www.foodproductiondaily.com/Quality-Safety/Study-raises-fruit-juice- pesticideconcerns?utm_source=copyright&utm_ medium=OnSite&utm_campaign=copyright.

2   Benachour, Nora, Emilie Clair, Robiin Mesnage and Gilles-Eric Seralini. Berhardt, Leon V. Editor. "Endocrine Disruptors: New Discoveries and Possible progress of Evaluation." Chapter 1, Advances in Medicine and Biology. Volume 29. Nova Science Publishers. Inc. 2012

3   Preidt, Robert. "Agricultural Chemical Spray Linked to Birth Defect Risk: Infant abdominal hernia rates higher near farms using atrazine, research shows." Health Tools. February 5, 2010. http://healthtools.aarp.org/healthday/agricultural-chemical-spray-linked-to-birth-defect-risk

4   Heeren, Gudrun A., Joanne Tyler and Andrew Mandeya. "Agricultural chemical exposures and birth defects in the Eastern Cape Province, South Africa A case—control study" Environmental Health: A Global Access Science Source 2003, 2:11 http://www.ehjournal.net/content/2/1/11

5   Richard Cutler, PhD, NIH, National Cancer Institute, "Antioxidants and Cancer Prevention: Fact Sheet", 28 July 2004.

6   Diamanti-Kandarakis E Et al. Endocrine-Disrupting Chemicals. An Endocrine Society Scienfific Statement. The Endocrine Society. 2009 endocrine Reviews 30(4):293-342. http://www.endo- society.org/journals/scientific state-ments/upload/edc_scientific_statement.pdf

Chapter 21
Sanitation, Pathogens, and Parasites

It is regularly stated by pundits of the "green revolution" in agriculture that everything is just fine because we are all living longer. The inference is that agricultural, industrial and medical technology is benign and in fact life promoting; that all the hype from the "greenies" about the dangers of pesticides, industrial chemicals, genetic engineered crops and drugs in our foods and environment is just political nonsense. What these pundits completely fail to recognize is that all but just three to four years of our increase life expectancy between 1900 and 2000 is completely accounted for by public health improvements, most importantly water and sewer sanitation. Older people today don't live any longer than older people in the 1700s. The founding fathers of the United States of America were a prime example. Two lived to 90 or more, three into their 80s.

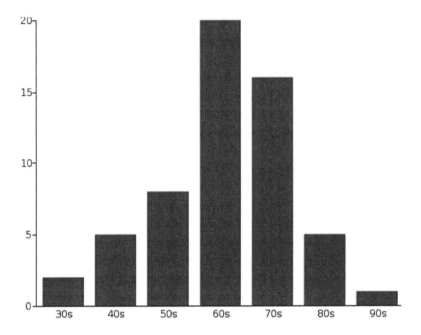

The problem during the 1700s and 1900s was that many children did not live to age ten, many young women died of childbirth. Life expectancy is an average so when one considers a significant percentage of the population dying by the early twenties, the average is quite low. Most of those babies, children and young mothers that died in 1900 would today, survive. The U.S. CDC showed that a 65-year-old person in 1900 had nearly as long a life expectancy as a 65 year old person today. Refer back to the life expectancy graph in chapter 2, "Nature Knows Best."

What is more concerning is that medical researchers today, estimate that the generation born today, will not live as long as it's parents. So much for all the wonderful advanced technology. This should not be at all surprising to any reader of this book. It is really very simple. It is all about nutrition, or actually the lack thereof. Healthy bodies require comprehensive nutrition. That nutrition is seriously lacking in today's modern high-tech food chain.

The degeneration of our food chain, whether by ignorance, accident, or intention has created a cesspool of toxicity around the world, on our farms, in our environment, and in our food. It has subsequently spawned a multi-trillion dollar industry, worldwide. Strong is the inertia to maintain this cash cow and slow is the acceptance to replace it with nutrition. But replace it we must, if we expect to survive, literally another century on this planet. As pointed out in the discussion about genetically engineered foods and glyphosate, animal studies and animal periodicals universally report sterility and infertility problems in lab animals and commercial farm animals.

Human infertility clinics abound today where thirty years ago they were few and far between. Some delusional humanitarians believe this is good for world population control, even decline and fully justified. What they fail to understand is that farmers only produce about 10 to 15 percent of the genetic potential of the crops they currently possess. Further, without increasing yield at all, we can feed the world easily at present by just improving the nutrient value of the food so it doesn't spoil. Distribution is the cause of starvation at the present time, not food supply. Increased nutrient value food requires less food per person to nourish that person so we would need even less food than we produce at present. Increase the production of nutrient dense food to the genetic potential of the crops we have, which can only be done via nutritional means, and we are capable of feeding many times the current world population well.

Yes, there are many parasitic and amoebic infections associated especially with the third world. Don't be lulled into believing they don't also exist in the developed world. Those are sanitation, public health issues. As proven in nutrient dense organic dairy operations, parasites are not a problem and don't require anti-parasitic drugs to treat because the animal nutrition allows the animals to produce protective immunity. This immunity is via skin oil and healthy protective microbiology.

Parasite cycles are broken with appropriate grazing management specifically not grazing the pasture too short. Manure is low in free nitrogen that attracts flies and breaks down rapidly preventing fly cycles from occurring. Organizations such as Organic Valley via Paul Dettloff, Circul8, and Tainio Technology have proven that proper manure management and lagoon operation not only completely eliminates foul odors, it converts animal waste into clean, safe fertilizer, breaks disease and fly cycles and prevents environmental pollution.

I wish to leave the reader both with a somber realization of how devastating the current food system is to human and animal health and our environment. Make no mistake about it, it is perilous. At the same time, I desire to give the reader an understanding that this perilous situation is fully arrestable, fully reversible, and fully feasible to correct quickly, economically, and realistically. With knowledge comes power and responsibility.

Knowing that genetically engineered crops are toxic and that glyphosate and other pesticides are as well enables the consumer to make different choices, to vote differently with his/her dollars at the grocery store. As consumers, our dollars spent at the grocery store are the ultimate vote for whatever is or will be on the shelf.

We truly live in an exciting time. There are some wonderful and amazing technologies expanding in agriculture today that are working toward reversing these problems. In physics, it is often stated that for every force there is an equal and opposite force. Know that for all the destructive force of GMOs, glyphosate, and all the chemical weapons industry with its intellectual prostitutes and patsys, there is an equal and opposite constructive force revitalizing our soils, environment and foods and, subsequently, revitalizing you and I with regenerative food.

Chapter 22

Recommendations

"One need not see the top of the stairs to take the first step."

—Rev. Martin Luther King

Get educated. That education will not come from the standard media or the typical university bulletins. There are a few places on the web where one can get information. They include, but not limited to, www.realfoodcampaign.org, www.remineralize.org, www.westonaprice.org, www.organicconsumers.org, www.sustainableagriculture.net, www.naturallygrown.org and www.acresusa.com to name a few. Information from these sites is, for the most part excellent; however, there are times when their personal political agendas overshadow the information that needs to be conveyed.

Understand what is covered in this book and get into the grocery store, the CSA, the farmer's market and observe, take
notes. Note what fruits and vegetables last the best in the refrigerator or on the counter. The ones that last the longest
have the better nutrition. Don't be fooled by unknowing
growers that tell you crappy looking fruits and vegetables
may look bad, but they are better because they are "organic."
Or not to worry about a little worm in the fruit or veggie because if it is safe for the worm to eat it is safe for you to eat.
That is all FICTION.

Truly high quality, nutrient dense ORGANIC produce looks
great, is free of insects, taste great, and is less filling. Actually
it is more fulfilling, more satisfying without the bloated feeling. Pay attention to what these better foods taste like? How
do you feel after eating these foods? Note how they cook,
their fragrance? Notice how the children like these fruits and
vegetables. How do they feel? Do they seem heavy for their
size? The heavier they are for their size the more nutrient
dense are the fruits and vegetables.

Avoid genetically engineered/modified foods as the plague.
This includes anything associated with corn, soybean, canola,

cotton seed, Hawaiian papaya, and alfalfa and any animals eating these genetically engineered crops. If the label is not "organic" or specifically says "non-GMO," avoid that food product as the plague.

Seek out the organic grass-fed meats. The next step down would be organic meats because at least they are feeding non-GMO grains. I will clarify. Most grass fed farmers graze their animals up until the last few months before slaughter and then put them in a feedlot to fatten the animal. Unless they are "organic" they will be feeding GMO grains in the feedlot. Even organic farmers claiming to have grass-fed meats send their animals to the feedlot for fattening. Granted, the organic grains are better than GMO grains, but the beef is still grain-fed, not grass-fed.

Ideally they would have high enough quality pasture that they wouldn't need to put the animals in the feedlot to fatten them as grain increases the saturated fat. The reality is that most of these cattle raisers don't have high-brix pasture or forage and/or don't understand such things. Consequently, they still fatten the animals on grain before slaughter. Be sure there were no synthetic growth hormones, estrogen or antibiotics used to grow the meat. Obviously for the vegetarians reading this book, this is a non-issue because you don't eat meat anyway. Visit: www.nongmoproject.org

Seek out the wild fish, avoiding the farm-raised fish. If the label says Atlantic salmon, it is farm raised unless proven otherwise. The same goes for catfish, shrimp, tilapia, and trout. They are farm raised unless proven otherwise. These farmers use GMO grains and antibiotics. Even more concerning, recently the genetically engineered fish were approved for human consumption.

Seek out A2 dairy products. Organic Valley is my recommended supplier of dairy products if you cannot specifically find A2 dairy products. Yes, there is the movement afoot suggesting you seek out raw dairy products. I agree that raw dairy is better digested, retains more important nutrition, and frankly tastes better. I was raised on raw milk straight from the bulk tank. The problem arises that producers are not always taking care of business and business, in this case, means getting the brix of the pasture above 12, feeding the cows free choice minerals and kelp, and abiding by good sanitary practices. This is a huge problem in the raw milk arena. Its pundits religiously promote all raw milk as the savior of human health.

There are significant public health risks when farmers fail to feed high-brix forage, fail to feed free-choice mineral and kelp, and fail in fundamental sanitation. Pasteurization is an excuse to sell dirty milk, but taking that same dirty milk and selling it as raw milk, insisting it is now somehow "pristine" just because it hasn't been pasteurized is nonsense. One must FIRST produce a quality product, before selling and claiming a quality product. I know high-brix, raw A2 milk is best, therapeutic, and desirable. I have no problem with quality, safe, raw milk. The milk brix should be 16 or above. The higher the milk brix, the healthier will be the cow, the more nutritious will be the milk, and, consequently, the lower the risk for contaminating species of bacteria to be present. Demand the better quality milk and eventually the farmers will have to supply it. The consumer's purchasing money talks!

There is a caveat discussion here. It is about undenatured whey. It has been proven therapeutic for people that can't maintain weight such as cancer patients and intestinal disorder patients. ImmunoCal is presently the ONLY company with this product. It is not the same as that whey one gets at the health food store. ImmunoCal is an immune booster. Part of its uniqueness is its tertiary structure. It cannot be blended vigorously; rather, it must be mixed gently with a spoon or you will break the structure and render the product no different than the health food store product.

There is a movement afoot to bring A2 undenatured whey to the market in 2013 so there will be two products available for persons in need. This is an exciting occurrence. Many more people will have access to this great medicinal product.

Chapter 23

The Solutions: "The Kitchen Gardener"

One may ask, "How are we going to correct these problems?" How can you the gardener, small or large farmer solve these problems? I will gear this discussion more to the consumer, the gardener, because there are professional seminars I teach for farmers that are serious about these solutions on their farms.

Most of the correction can be gotten from the grocery store so those folks doing potted gardens or window sill gardens, fear not, you too can do this art. I like to call it grocery store gardening. Let's look at our shopping list first. Milk (whole milk is preferred, any will do) or infant formula, apple cider vinegar, kelp, lactobacillus capsules, or yogurt, Coke (original, no diet versions), whey protein powder, free-range eggs, canned salmon with skin and bones, or sardines in oil or water, sea salt, nut butter (I prefer macadamia nut butter personally), 20

Mule Team borax or a bottle of boric acid, and a bag of sugar. At the health food store, pick up a bottle of Trace Mineral Drops, Atomodine or iodine drops, colloidal silver, digestive enzymes in capsules, Emergen-C packets (any flavor you prefer), and some fulvic acid (get it in the health food store usually packaged as "liquid minerals") if you can get it reasonably. Note that most everything is edible, as it should be, other than the Borax, but the boric acid will do and is used for eye wash.

We want to prepare the soil for planting seed or transplants. The mix we are about to prepare will be applied to the soil and gently mixed into the top 2 to 4 inches whether pots or garden beds. Take out the blender, put in a quart of milk (calcium, phosphorous, a few traces, lactose sugar), two cans of salmon or equivalent of sardines (calcium and phosphorous, some trace elements, oil, protein or nitrogen), a couple eggs (protein or nitrogen and sulfur), a quarter of a teaspoon of borax or boric acid (boron), 10 to 20 capsules of digestive enzymes, 10 to 20 capsules of lactobacillus or one 8-ounce container of yogurt, 1 tablespoon of fulvic acid, 1 teaspoon of crushed seaweed, ¼ cup of whey protein (nitrogen), 1 teaspoon of trace mineral drops, and 1 cup of apple cider vinegar. Add filtered or spring water (no chlorinated water) to make up a half gallon or more depending upon your blender size.

You could add any table scraps left over from any fruits or vegetables served for a meal. Blend until completely smooth and let sit for at least an hour before applying to the soil. Some organic farmers are using peanut meal as a nitrogen source that works well, the only problem is that it tends to be high in aflotoxins unless cooked.

You could of course drink this if you wanted, which is the point. It's safe. You would now apply this "smoothie blend" to your garden area of 500 to 1000 square feet or 1 to 2 table-spoons to a pot of soil. Obviously for the real small areas, you would mix up a smaller batch of this blend. This blend can be applied and lightly worked into the soil every week or two throughout the season if necessary. Necessary meaning we need more boost for plant growth.

One could make it simpler and just use whey protein powder as the nitrogen source and apply it dry or liquid weekly or every two weeks as needed. If you get too much nitrogen, you will have aphids attacking the plants. Aphids indicate there is more nitrogen in relation to other nutrients necessary for the plant to convert the nitrogen to complete proteins. The whey will be broken down by soil bacteria and plant leaf bacteria if you apply this mix to the leaf. This whey will be converted to nitrate and ammonia nitrogen or simpler amino acids that the plant takes in and utilizes to make its own amino acids and proteins. The point of putting in many different ingredients is to have a broader spectrum of vitamins and minerals for enhancing the soil, which ultimately enhances the nutrient value of the food grown on that soil. Note: Cats will smell the fish and come calling to your garden.

Additionally, we want to foliar spray the plants especially if we have seed or fruiting plants such as beans, peas, tomatoes, melons, squash, cucumbers, okra, strawberries, raspberries, blueberries, tree fruit, etc. The success with foliar spray fertilization/feeding depends upon understanding a little about the birds and the bees, the difference between boys-male and girls-female. I know this is a touchy and complicated subject, just bear with me for a moment, please.

Leafy vegetables that we harvest for greens, NOT SEED, must be kept "male." This means they must be kept in the growth or vegetative stage. If we allow them or force them to convert to "female" they will bolt and produce seed. To keep them "male" we use calcium and potassium as our primary "masculine" materials. As such, milk is our primary ingredient in foliar sprays for leafy vegetables such as lettuce, spinach, broccoli, cauliflower, cabbage, kale, and bok choy.

Add milk to a standard pint or quart spray bottle commonly used in the kitchen for window spray, (be sure it is clean). It can be sprayed straight on the plants. Milk can also be diluted 1 to 1 up to 1 to 10 with filtered or spring water. To this milk/water mix, add a teaspoon of trace mineral drops, a tablespoon of plain yogurt, or several capsules of lactobacillus probiotic and a pinch of seaweed powder. Replace the spray top to the bottle and mix or shake gently to mix all ingredients. Take this mix and mist the plants twice weekly or at least during the two weeks of the increase in the moon, between the new moon and the full moon. You don't need to wash the plants with this milk mix, just mist them just up to the point where the leaves would drip. This is ideally done late in the day, preferably after 8:00 p.m.

This same spray can be applied to all the fruit and seed crops, but you will need to alternate with the "female" spray, otherwise the plants won't produce much seed or fruit. Most gardeners have probably had a season where their tomatoes or melons or seed/fruit crops had great plants, lush growth, but few or no fruit. The weather was blamed, the variety was blamed, or something other than the truth was blamed for the failure to produce fruit. The reality is that the plants remained "male" and never converted to "female" during the season. This is entirely a fertilizer issue.

The "fruit set" or "female" foliar mix is nearly as simple as the "male" mix, but more complex as one would expect. This is where the Coke comes in to the mix. Take a clean spray 1-quart spray bottle, fill half with filtered water, and add 1 to 2 teaspoons of household ammonia or a scoop of your favorite protein powder. Mix gently. Add the 12-ounce bottle of Coke, the real thing, not that with corn sugar as that will be a genetically modified source of sweetener. (As a side note, sugar beets are now genetically modified and sprayed with glyphosate so beet sugar is out. Further, many cane sugar growers now spray the cane with glyphosate/RoundUp prior to harvesting because they are no longer allowed to burn the cane.

This leaves us with glyphosate in the molasses and possibly the sugar; therefore if you are going to use sugar, use organic sugar.) If you have aphids or are concerned about aphids, add 1/2 teaspoon of Epsom salts to the spray mix. To this add 1 tablespoon of apple cider vinegar and mix gently. Add a teaspoon of trace mineral drops and mix gently, add a drop of iodine (especially for carrots), a pinch of seaweed (plant growth stimulants), 1 teaspoon of fulvic acid (a great nutrient chelator and microbial food), and a dropper full of B12 (feeds the microbes) which you can obtain from Crossroads Healing Arts. If you want to boost it more, add a teaspoon of Royal Jelly as the last ingredient in this mix.

Mist the plants with this mix twice weekly and once weekly with the milk spray mix. If still after a week the plants are not setting fruit and flushing flowers then add 2 to 4 additional tablespoons of apple cider vinegar to the spray mix. Note: If you use protein powder, you may want to put it in water and in a blender to be sure it is thoroughly mixed before adding anything else because if not thoroughly mixed it may plug your spray nozzle.

The purists will grumble about the use of Coke. It is a great tonic by the way if you have Montezuma's revenge from travel in Mexico or elsewhere. It settles the stomach and provides valuable emergency electrolytes. I don't recommend drinking it any other time. Coke contains sugar to feed the beneficial microbes on the leaf, phosphoric acid to feed the microbes and the plant, carbon dioxide to feed the plant (remember plants take in CO_2 and produce O_2), and caffeine, which increases protein synthesis. It is a great foliar fertilizer in and by itself. Keep in mind that we are interested in nutrition, raising plant brix levels and producing the absolute most nutritious food possible. Of course, if you want to get "organic certification" you cannot use Coke in the mix, but it still works great and will give you better health plants. Instead of the Coke, you can obtain fish emulsion, some brewed organic coffee, protein powder, and organic sugar along with carbonated/sparkling water.

The Coke issue is just a discussion about philosophical dogma, not nutrient quality of food. As already mentioned in an earlier chapter, organic certification is about following a dogmatic procedure, not about outcome. Oh, and what about the nut butter mentioned on the grocery list? Take celery sticks and dip them in the nut butter and enjoy as a snack in between tasks. It is a great low-glycemic snack.

I mentioned the phase of the moon. Plants respond most to foliar feeding on the increase of the moon (new moon to full moon), less so on the decrease of the moon (full moon to new moon) The moon phases are quite important as one gets more sophisticated in his/her gardening, not to say that one cannot have a very successful garden without observing moon phases. Celestial cycles are powerful electromagnetic and gravitational influences on all life on this planet. I suggest using every means available to improve the outcome of our food producing endeavors. I suggest that when transplanting plants bought from the local garden store including vegetable plants, ornamentals or trees, that a little yogurt or milk (1/4 cup), enzymes (4 to 5 capsules) be watered into the soil.

I recommend purchasing Rescue Remedy and Arnica homeopathic drops or sugar pills and applying those in the first watering as well at the same dose recommended on the package. Transplanting is literally a shocking experience for plants. It stresses them. The homeopathics will help to relieve this stress and allow the plant to take off growing sooner. This can

also be added to the foliar spray given after each pick-
ing/harvest or lawn mowing. I know this sounds a bit odd, but
plants respond very affirmatively to homeopathic remedies.

The above recommendations for a soil blend, foliar sprays
and transplanting are basic approaches that will be successful
wherever one resides. If one wants to get a little more sophisticated with his/her gardening whether in pots, beds or small
truck farm, a little more study is beneficial.

Understanding some basic principles will help the beginner
grasp what needs to be achieved. Like medical physical exam
and diagnosis, soil and plants convey to the keen observer
what is going on with them. Look at your lawn. If your
chemical lawn agent did not spray herbicide or you did not
apply "weed and feed" bagged granules from the lawn and
garden store, would you see weeds growing in your lawn?
Most of you would. Why? Because you have a herbicide deficiency? No! The grasses being grown are higher successional species than the weeds so this means your lawn soil is
at a lower successional level than needed. Your soil is too
compact and you have a higher bacterial biomass than benefi-

cial fungi. This soil needs some work. First it needs calcium, functional nutrient calcium.

Your County Extension Agent or garden store sales person hasn't a clue. They will ask you, "What is your soil pH?" If it is near 7, they will tell you that you don't need lime. Clarification here, I did not suggest you needed to add lime to alter the soil pH. This quickly becomes and Abbott and Costello debate. "Who's on first, I don't know's on second, etc." I don't really care what is the soil pH as long as it is between 5 and 9. I know you need functional nutrient calcium because you have weeds in a grass lawn. For grass to truly be healthy, it needs a lot of calcium. Calcium flocculates the soil, allowing it to open up and "breathe," which subsequently allows the beneficial microbes, especially beneficial fungi to flourish. This equally applies to your potted plants and raised bed gardens. Calcium is the foundation to healthy plants.

One of the best sources for the small gardener and lawn connoisseur is milk, as already discussed earlier; yes the milk you buy at the grocery store. Apply about a cup to a quart per 1,000 square feet through the sprinkler system, weekly. For your garden and potted veggies, put a quart of milk into a gallon of water and water weekly with this mix. Purchase capsules of probiotic, lactobacillus, and put in 2 to 4 capsules and mix before application. If one wants to be a little more sophisticated, use infant formula though it will be a bit more expensive.

At pre-plant, apply the blender mix described above and follow-up with the foliar sprays described. To get more sophisticated, one can purchase soil amendments and foliar mixes from reputable farm and garden suppliers including, but not limited to Lancaster Ag Products in Lancaster, PA., www.lancasterag.com (excellent dry blend garden package), Nitron Industries in Fayetteville, Arkansas, www.nitron.com, ARBICO in Tucson, Arizona, www.arbico-organics.com (they also raise and sell beneficial insects), Tainio Technologies, Spokane, Washington, www.tainio.com (they have plant organic fertilizer tablets (BioPellets) that are excellent for potted plants and great microbial inoculants), Advancing Eco Agriculture in Middlefield, Ohio, www.growbetterfood.com, MicroLife Organic Fertilizers from San Jacinto Environmental Supplies, Houston, Texas, www.sanjacsuppply.com, FHR in Stewartville, Minnesota, www.fhr1.com.

It is important to learn to observe soils and plants. What do you see? What do you sense? Everything occurs for a reason. Weeds are there as nature's means for balancing the soil though it may take 1,000 years. Discern what is happening and manage appropriately to balance that soil in a few years. Sour grass weeds such as foxtail, nutgrass, quackgrass, Johnsongrass, etc., are all indicators of functional calcium deficiency even on calcitic soils.

You may have plenty of calcium rock sitting there, but a significant deficiency in functional calcium. Think of the calcium in your body settled out as spurs and calcium deposits. It is calcium, but doing you little good, nutritionally. To get this calcium functional in the soil, you need small amounts of functional calcium, milk is a good source potentially, enzymes and probiotics to activate the calcium, and trace elements to complete the puzzle. Treat the plants, your "patients," not the lab numbers. Think of yourself as a patient. Do you want to be treated as an individual person or some lab number on a piece of paper?

Insect and diseases are present because of abstract nutrient deficiencies/imbalances. Learn what they are and then address them in your foliar sprays. Your local Cooperative Extension Service office does have excellent publications with color pictures of plant nutrient deficiency symptoms. Learn to recognize these symptoms, but take it the next step and always ask, "Why are these symptoms present?" Don't just treat the symptom, although that is sometimes appropriate. Learn about various mineral sources, paramagnetic rock (Phil Callahan: Ancient Mysteries, Modern Visions), learn about human digestive issues, probiotics, pathogen-antagonist microbial relationships, observe the plants, test their sap with a refractometer.

Whatever you do, the goal is to increase plant sap brix readings. If you are not doing that, you must change course, reassess, adjust your mixes, whatever it takes to get the brix readings to increase. Plant sap/juice brix readings to nutrient density. Ultimately, that is all that really counts, that we are increasing the nutrient density of the food. All else is fluff and philosophy that does nothing for our personal nutritional status. So keep your eye on the ball, so to speak, and the ball is the plant sap brix level. www.highbrixgardens.com has a brix chart for various garden plants for your reference.

I know that many of you simply go to the garden section at whatever store you frequent and buy whatever fertilizer blend, dry or dry soluble, they have on the shelf or in the bag. First of all, check the label, if they are using potassium chloride as the potassium source, don't buy it. It is cheap, that's why they use it, and pretty much guarantees you won't achieve the quality results discussed in this book. Second, some of these dry soluble materials can be made to work just fine if you modify them a bit. Certainly they are not "organic" so the purists will roll over in their grave, but I am interested in results, not fluff, buff and philosophy.

Dry soluble fertilizers are generally N-P-K (nitrogen-phosphorus-potassium) blends with a few trace elements added such as manganese, copper, iron, and zinc. It is more label dressing than substance and satisfies the state fertilizer commission labeling laws. Let's say you get Miracle-Gro, simple to use, great advertising, and does stimulate the plant. Problem is it can also imbalance the plant. To this mix, in the 1-quart spray bottle, add 1 to 2 tablespoons of vinegar, a teaspoon of sugar, yes table sugar, a pinch of kelp, 1 to 2 teaspoons of fulvic acid, 1 to 2 teaspoons of trace mineral drops. One could add a half or full 12-ounce can/bottle of Coke.

This mix can now be a reasonable spray. Check the plant sap brix level with your refractometer to monitor the plant health and progress with the nutritional spray.

Once we are through the growing season, we want to "put the soil to bed" for the winter. Chop up the dead or dying remaining plants/vines and spread them over the soil. Spray with a mixture of 1 gallon water, ¼ cup protein powder, 1 tablespoon sugar, 10 capsules digestive enzymes, and 10 capsules probiotics and spray over 500 to 1000 square foot garden. You can add more water if need and even more material if desired. If you want to get more sophisticated, purchase the residue digester and enzymes from Tainio.com and use that as your inoculant and enzymes rather than the probiotics and enzymes from the health food store. Tainio's soil probiotic will be stronger and more specific for the soil if you desire that or have a larger area.

Once the spray is applied, gently mix the crop residue into the top 2 to 4 inches of soil and plant to oats, clover and Austrian peas or oats and vetch or oats and clover or oats alone as the cover crop. In the spring, you can incorporate the winter cover crop into the soil. It is possible to actually keep this cover crop going, other than the oats and plant directly into it in the spring, mowing in at 4 to 5 inches high helping to keep weeds down and protect your young garden plants. You can place bales of hay or straw on the ground and use them as the base for raised beds. You would apply a couple inches of potting mix over the top and plant into it. The plant roots will extend into the bales and down into the ground. It is recommended that the bales be "conditioned" first with some fertilizer to start a digesting process. This could be the "smoothie blend" I described earlier poured over the top of the bales and lightly watered into the bales. It could be a purchased dry blend from one of the companies mentioned above.

I like the green manure incorporation into the soil as it builds the soil faster and then apply mulch around your garden plants to control weeds and conserve moisture. Be aware that if you use grass clippings from a lawn that has had herbicide applied you could be applying that herbicide to your garden as a residue in the grass clippings. This will stunt your garden plants.

Avoid using wood ash to any extended amount as this dehydrates the soil and can potentially imbalance the phosphorous to potassium ratio causing more broadleaf weeds to grow, frustrating you even more regarding weed control. Wood mulch and wood ash as well as woody compost, actually most compost, will be higher in potassium, which must be taken into consideration for balance with calcium, phosphorous, and magnesium. Too much potash, potassium, and you will have great broadleaf weeds growing, difficulty in getting plant sap brix to come up, insect and disease pressures and overall frustration with the lack of progress in superior nutrient density. Yes, it might be natural and organic and all that nice rhetoric but not nutrient dense as we need it. Just be sure to keep the calcium coming.

If you get too much magnesium, you will have a problem stabilizing nitrogen, but on the other hand if you have problems with aphids that means you have too much free nitrate nitrogen, organic or not, and need to add a teaspoon to a tablespoon of Epsom salts to your foliar mix.

If you notice that your vine crops are just growing wildly with long intervals between nodes, hit them with the female foliar mix with the upper limit 1 tablespoon of Epsom salts. If after a week of two of these sprays these plants are still growing wildly, double the Epsom salts in the mix for the following week. If still the plants are growing wildly, double the vinegar and perhaps prune back the plants a bit. Get some Coke or suitable alternative in the mix as we need some available phosphorous and caffeine to promote protein synthesis of this free nitrate nitrogen. You may not have used any chemical fertilizer for this to happen. You could have used compost and fish. It is a dynamic between male and female out of balance. Understand that concept and you will be well on your way to successful nutrient dense growing management.

The next more sophisticated thing one can do is treating the seed and transplants. A probiotic inoculant is preferred so if you go to the health food store and find "soil-based probiotics" that would be desirable. Put your seeds into a zip-lock back and add a couple capsules of these soil base probiotics and shake just as you would if you were coating chicken in a bag with corn meal or flour. These seeds are then ready to be planted. One can also purchase a seed inoculant from the various companies mentioned. The same holds true for the transplants except they will not be put in a bag, rather just put a dusting of the microbes on the root mass before planting.

One can get the microbial pellets from Tainio.com and put one with each root mass upon planting. Add the homeopathics to the first watering along with more probiotics and the plants will get off to a faster start.

I recommend that you purchase heritage seeds and treat them with the probiotics and the nutrient program outlined previously. These seeds have the lowest possibility of having contamination from genetically engineered plants and have the best genetics for maximizing potential nutrient density.

It is important to understand that just going back to nature does not ensure that one will have food fit to eat. There are many places on this planet, in natural settings, where the soil is very primitive and unfit for growing higher successional food plants we need. Read the plants in your garden or lawn setting, they will tell you what is needed if you are paying attention. Don't be misled by the rhetoric of natural, organic, etc., when your plant brix are low and you are inundated by weeds, insect pests, diseases, and the like. These problems are messages for you to heed.

I was shopping at a farmer's market in Arkansas one time many years ago, stopped by a booth where the farmer was selling "organic" apples. They looked poor. The farmer was a bit perturbed by my expressions in looking at the apples and informed me that if there were a worm in the apple it meant that the apple was safe from pesticides and good for me to eat. I politely explained to the farmer that if the worm was eating the apple it meant just the opposite, the apple was NOT fit for me to eat, nutritionally speaking, and this was nature's garbage collector recycling that which needed recycling for when the nutrient density of the apple reached a threshold, the worm would no longer be attracted to the apple and it would be sufficient for me to eat and maintain good health. He was not interested nor did he want to hear about such nonsense. He was an organic farmer and he knew better.

It is sad so many organic farmers are equally, and in some cases, more uninformed about soil and plant nutrition than conventional chemical farmers. Philosophy is so comfortable to hold onto, so nice and touchy-feely to ponder when sitting around a fireplace in the middle of winter sipping on a cup of tea or hot chocolate. It fits so nicely in the "save the world" rhetoric, but as rhetoric it has no substance in nutrient density, realistic farm/garden production or actual regeneration of the soil and environment. Very simply, if the brix levels of the sap/juice are not increasing to the "excellent" range whatever you are doing is not getting the job done and is NOT regenerating the food chain, your body or the environment. It is that simple and straightforward.

There are organic farmers getting the job done: Mark Nakata growing organic tree fruit in California, Jason and Yvonne Kimm growing organic potatoes in Montana, Uncle Matt's growing organic citrus and peaches in Florida, Ed Huling growing organic tomatoes in New York, and John Kempf growing nutrient dense vegetables in Ohio, just to name a few. These farmers didn't drink the "organic Kool-Aid" and just get lucky with great soil. They worked to understand science and the real goal for food production, nutrient dense food and set out to get that job done. Their quest continues and they have proven that organics can both produce better nutrient density and compete with any conventional program in cost per unit of production, yield and sustainability. There are a few companies out there that are doing a great job applying the principles I have mentioned. They are growing as their results in the field, greenhouse, garden, and barn speak for themselves.

We are truly faced with a 21st century Food Plague. Genetically engineered crops coupled with glyphosate and similar chemical weapons being applied to our soils and food crops are the greatest threat to the survival of humankind, in my opinion, that this world has ever faced, greater yet than the bubonic plague and the avian flu epidemics of centuries past. As with all challenges, we have the solutions within our midst.

Like every generation before us and probably every generation after us, it seems that 10 percent of the people are the movers and shakers, the pioneers, those with the most arrows in their backs. The next 10 percent are early adaptors of what the pioneers have discovered, still with arrows in their back, just fewer than the pioneers. The next 60 percent are the fence sitters that will come along as the wind blows, when they think it is the way of the masses, "everybody else is doing it." The next 10 percent are the late adaptors. They take a long time to finally realize that change is in their best interest and then there is the last 10 percent that shoot the most arrows and will never change regardless of the science, the proof, or the economics. They will have to die off for the space that they occupy to change.

We are still in the pioneering and early adaptor phases of changing our food chain for the better. The inertia is very strong toward the destruction of our food chain from a hundred years of decline. It is so profitable for a few that they will do literally anything they must to keep the trend going until their own death. False prophecies eventually implode and self-destruct. We are nearing that implosion as Dr. Don Huber points out with more rampant crop disease, resistant weeds, diseases and insect pests, with less and less success with more and more of the chemical weapons.

I realize that we live today in a society of convenience, quick fixes, silver bullets, and personal responsibility abstinence. As a result, it is seen as nearly impossible to achieve the natural balance I discuss in this book. The prevention and correction of weeds, diseases and insect pests is seen as mere theory, something completely out of touch with reality. It truly is for some people. It is nonetheless feasible, practical and achievable for those that study, pay attention and get busy doing what is necessary to improve the soil and plant health.

Keep in mind that the naysayers are never going to help you achieve what they themselves cannot envision or don't want to achieve. Every consumer contributes to either the naysayer or the problem solver by what he or she purchases at the grocery store, CSA or farmer's market. It's your vote, spend it wisely.

Contributing to the shift is the shifting demand from the public voting daily at the grocery store with their money. That is truly the most important vote. Each and every one of us has the power of purchase. That vote determines what the retailers put on their shelves, what they demand from the producer. Education fuels demand, which precipitates supply. We consumers have the power, we just need to recognize it and use it. I bid you successful gardening, judicious purchasing, and most importantly high-brix, nutrient-dense dining.

There are many reasons espoused daily by the media for one to be depressed and perhaps hopeless. Know that every problem is solvable. We have the technology and the will to grow better food and regenerate our environment. Yes, perhaps there is considerable evil dispersed throughout society, in corporate boardrooms, in political offices, in university class-rooms, on city streets or perhaps in the car racing by you on the highway. Each person has free will to choose whether to participate in that status quo or step out and exercise benevo-lence. These are exciting times, not just interesting times. This is the generation that will get suppressed free-energy technology and cancer cures into the public realm; will get regenerative agriculture and food production into the public dining experience.

Keep heart and read the book, *Proof of Heaven* by Eben Al-exander, M.D. Your spirit will be revived and your hope re-turned.

The Food We Eat

Environment determines genetic expression,
For many this causes great depression.
Food pervades our every environment,
Sadly sending many to early retirement
Blame thy ancestors for the DNA they display
Eat what you want and be on your way
That is the mantra of the doctor today
Scripting drugs the cartels display
To what then do we owe the genes,
Only to ourselves for we employ the means
For what we eat determines our fate
Though many would say that's up for debate
We are the ones who make the choices
For health or many false voices
There is nothing wrong with the gene code
If man will cease his conniving mode
It is he who pollutes and pillages;
Spraying pesticides over entire villages.
We hear of suffering and the frequent birth defect,

Yet the FDA says not to worry for you we will protect.

Experts abound with their well-greased palms,

Quoting chemical mantras as if they were the Psalms.

Man must intervene we are told,

To feed the world with GE fields of gold

Many are they these false prophets of chemistry,

Decorated as if they were in the ministry;

Drunk with their renewable money grants,

They fail to see the foolishness of their rants.

For to nature we can look,

As we would study, the Good Book.

She will reveal our God-given destiny,

as if we were struck by an epiphany;

To the field, nature sends the insect,

Perfectly designed to clean up our neglect;

She sends in the weed,

To regenerate, the soil's greatest need;

It is nutrition that's our foundation and fundamental feed,

For without nutrition, we die a slow and withering bleed.

We have the technology and the means,

To heal our soil and grow great greens;

It's really what we eat, that determines our genes

We must act with purpose each and every day,

Or surely, we will have no energy, for which to play;

High-brix food

Gives us good mood;

And a healthy good life

Without all the strife

We can have it all,

Without hitting the wall;

If we once and for all,

Keep our eye on the nutritional ball.

Food's meant to be our friend

Upon which we can fully depend

To keep us pure

Through all we must endure

The foolish whims of man's degrade

The genetic blue print that God has made

As Stiener said when he was asked

Why weak minds, fail to fully grasp

The basic truth, of this learning task

The mineral, is gone from their table

To think and reason they are not fully able

Still it's the choices, we willfully make

What ingredients we will put, into the cake

Those nutrients, do determine the fate

Of the genes, with us 'til the end of date

APPENDIX

Some Selected References on Glyphosate

1.   AgroNews. 2011. India: Signs of food toxicity in GE eggplant. Scoop.co.nz 2011-1-18. [http://news.agropages.com/News/NewsDetail---3369.htm] Nib, 24 January 111.

2.   Ananda, R. 2011. Scientists warn of link between dangerous new pathogen and Monsanto's RoundUp. Pp. 1-7. Food Freedom. http://foodfreedom.wordpress.com/2011/02/20/roundup-new-pathogen/

3.   Ananda, R. 2011. More problems with glyphosate: US rice growers sound the alarm. Global Research, May 15, 2011. http://www.Globalresearch.ca/printArticle.php?articleId=24775

4.   Anonymous, 11 April 2002. Unexplained abortion and abnormal ageing in cattle. http://www.vetscite.org/publish/items/000516/

5.   Antoniou, M. Brack, P., Carrasco, A., Fagan, J., Habib, M., Kageyama, P., Leifert, C., Onofre, N., and Penegue, W. 2010. GM Soy: Sustainable? Responsible? Report, GLS Gemeinschaftsbank eG and ARGE Gentechnik-frei 2010.

6.   Antoniou, M. Habib, M.E.E,M., Howard, V., Jennings,
      R.C., Leifert, C., Nodari, R.., Robinson, C., and Fagan,
      J. 2011. RoundUp and birth defects: is the public being
      kept in the dark? Earth Open Source, June 2011.
      http://scribd.com/doc57277946/RoundUpandBirthDefec
      tsv5

7.   Arregui, M.C., Lenardon, A., Sanchez, D., Maitre, M.I.,
      Scotta, R., and Enrique, S. 2003. Monitoring glyphosate
      residues in transgenic glyphosate-resistant soybean. Pest
      Manag. Sci. 60:163-166.

8.   Aris, A. and Leblanc, S. 2011. Maternal and fetal expo-
      sure to pesticides associated to genetically modified
      foods in Eastern Townships of Quebec, Canada. Re-
      prod. Tocicol. (2011).
      Doi:10.1016/j.reprotox.2011.02.004.

9.   Bailey, W.A., Poston, D.H., Wilson, H.P., and Hines,
      T.E. 2002. Glyphosate interactions with manganese.
      Weed Tech. 16:792-799.

10.   Barker, B. 2010. Seed germination hurt with pre-harvest
      and desiccation applications. Glyphosate and Reglone
      residues were more prevalent in 2009. Top Crop Man-
      ager (West): February 2010:78-80.

11.   Bellaloui, N., Reddy, K.N., Zablotowicz, R.M., Abbas,
      H.K., and Abel, C.A. 2009. Effects of glyphosate appli-
      cation on seed iron and root ferric (III) reductase in
      soybean cultivars. J. Agric. Food Chem. 57:9569-9574.

12. Benachour, N. Sipahutar, H., Moslemi, S., Gasnier, C., Travert, C., and Seralini, G.E. 2007. Time- and dose-dependent effects of roundup on human embryonic and placental cells. Arch. Environ. Contam. Toxicol. 53:126-133.

13. Benbrook, C. 1999. Evidence of the Magnitude and Consequences of the RoundUp Ready Soybean Yield Drag from University Based Varietal Trials in 1998. Ag BioTech InfoNet Technical Paper Number 1, July 13, 1999.

14. Bernards, M.L. Thelen, K.D., Muthukumaran, R.J. and McCracker, J.L. 2005. Glyphosate interaction with manganese in tank mixtures and its effect on glyphosate absorption and translocation. Weed Sci. 53:787-794.

15. Bott, S., Tesfamariam, T., Candan, H., Cakmak, I., Roemheld, V., and Neumann, G. 2008. Glyphosate-induced impairment of plant growth and micronutrient status in glyphosate-resistant soybean (Glycine max L.). Plant Soil 312:185-194.

16. Bott, S., Tesfamariam, T., Kania,, A. Eman, B., Aslan, N., Roemheld, V., and Neumann, G. 2011. Phytotoxicity of glyphosate soil residues re-mobilised by phosphate fertilization. Plant Soil 315:2-11. DOI 10, 1007/s11104-010-0689-3.

17. Boyette, C.D., Reddy, K.N., and Hoagland, R.E. 2006. Glyphosate and bioherbicide interaction for controlling kudzu (Pueraria lobata), and trumpet creeper (Campsis radicans). Biocontrol Sci. Tech. 16:1067-1077.

18.   Bramhall, R.A. and Higgins, V.J. 1988. The effect of
       glyphosate on resistance of tomato to Fusarium crown
       and root rot disease and on the formation of host struc-
       tural defensive barriers. Can. J. Bot. 66:1547-1555.

18.a. Brown, P. 2000. The promise of plant biotechnology
       and the threat of genetically modified organisms. Ag
       BioTech InfoNet. Available from <http://biotech-
       info.net/biotech_promise.html>

19.   Cakmak, I., Yazici, A., Tutus, Y., and Ozturk, L. 2009.
       Glyphosate reduced seed and leaf concentrations of cal-
       cium, magnesium, manganese, and iron in non-
       glyphosate resistant soybean. European J. Agron.
       31:114-119.

20.   Camberato, J., Wise, K., and Johnson, B. 2010. Glypho-
       sate-manganese interactions and impacts on crop pro-
       duction: the controversy. Purdue Extension Weed Sci.
       4/8/2010. www.btny.purdue.edu/weedscience.

21.   Camberato, J., Casteel, S., Goldsbrough, P., Johnson,
       B., Wise, K., Woloshuk, C. 2011. Glyphosate's impact
       on crop production and disease development. February
       24, 2011. www.btny.purdue.edu/weedscience/

22.   Chainark, P. (2008) Availability of genetically modified
       feed ingredient II: investigations of ingested foreign
       DNA in rainbow trout Oncorhynchus mykiss. Fisheries
       Sci., 74(2): 380-390(11).

23.   Chang, C-C., Simcik, M.F., Capel, P. 2011. Occur-
       erence and fate of the herbicide glyphosate and its de-

gradate aminomethylphosphonic acid in the atmosphere. Environ. Toxicol. Chem. 30:3:548-555.

24. Comeau, A., Pageau, D., Voldeng, H., and Brunelle, A. 2005. Micronutrients: essential for early canopy establishment in bread wheat. EECCO poster, Ottawa, Canada.

25. Coupland, D. and Caseley, J.C. 1979. Presence of 14 C activity in root exudates and guttation fluid from Agropyron repens treated with 14C-labeled glyphosate. New Phytol. 83:17-22.

26. Datnoff, L.E., Elmer, W.H., and Huber, D.M. (eds.). 2007. Mineral Nutrition and Plant Disease. APS Press, St. Paul, MN, 278 pages.

27. Dick, R.P., and Lorenz, N. 2006. Interactions of soil microbial biomass, mineralogy and organic matter with potassium dynamics of corn in rotation with glyphosate tolerant soybeans. Proc. Glyphosate Potassium Symposium, Ohio State Univ.

27.a. Diels, J., Cunha, M., Manaia, C., Sabugosa-Madeira, B., and Silva, M. 2011. Association of financial or professional conflict of interest to research outcomes on health risks or nutritional assessment studie4s of genetically modified products. Food Safety36:197-203.

28. Dodds, D.M., Hickman, M.V., and Huber, D.M. 2002. Comparison of micronutrient uptake by glyphosate resistant and non-resistant soybeans. Proc. North Central Weed Sci. Soc. 56:96.

29. Dodds, D.M., Hickman, M.V., and Huber, D.M. 2002, Micronutrient uptake by isogenic glyphosate tolerant and normal corn. Proc. Weed Sci. Soc. Amer. 42:2.

30. Duke, S.O., Rimando, A.M., Pace, P.F., Reddy, K.N., and Smeda, R.J. 2003. Isoflavone, glyphosate, and aminomethylphosphonic acid levels in seeds of glyphosate-treated, glyphosate-resistant soybean, J. Agric. Food Chem. 51:340-344.

30.a. Dunham, A. 2011. Trace mineral problems may lead to stillbirths and other herd health problems. Minnesota Dairy Health Conf. May 17-19, 2011, University of Minnesota College of Veterinary Medicine, St. Paul, MN.

31. EFSA. 2007. Statement on the fate of recombinant DNA or proteins in the meat, milk or eggs of animals fed with GM feed. http://www.efsa.europa.eu/en/scdocs/scdoc/744.htm.

32. Eker, S., Ozturk, L, Yazici, A., Erenoglu, B., Roemheld, V., and Cakmak, I. 2006. Foliar-applied glyphosate substantially reduced uptake and transport of iron and manganese in sunflower (Helianthus annuus L.) plants. J. Agric. Food Chem. 54:10019-10025.

33. Farenhorst, A., McQueen, D.A.R., Saiyed, I., Hilderbrand, C., Li, S., Lobb, D.A., Messing, P., Scumacher, T.E., Papiernik, S.K., Lindstrom, M.J. 2009. Variations in soil properties and herbicide sorption coefficients with depth in relation to PRZM (pesticide root zone model) calculations. Geoderma 150:267-277.

34. Feng, P.C.C., Baley, G.J., Clinton, W.P., Bunkers, G.J., Alibhai, M.F., Paulitz, T.C., and Kidwell, K.K. 2005. Glyphosate inhibits rust diseases in glyphosate-resistant wheat and soybean. Proc. Natl. Acad. Sci. 102:17290-17295.

35. Feng, P.C.C., Clark, C., Andrade, G.C., Balbi, M.C., and Caldwell, P. 2007. The control of Asian rust by glyphosate in glyphosate-resistant soybeans. Pest Manag. Sci. 64:353-359.

36. Fernandez, M.R., Selles, F., Gehl, D., DePauw, R.M., and Zentner, R.P. 2005. Crop production factors associated with Fusarium head blight in spring wheat in eastern Saskatchewan. Crop Sci. 45:1908-1916.

37. Fernandez, M.R., Zentner, R.P., DePauw, R.M., Gehl, D., and Stevenson, F.C. 2007. Impacts of crop production factors on Fusarium head blight in barley in Eastern Saskatchewan. Crop Sci. 47:1585-1595.

38. Fernandez, M.R., Kremer, R.J., Zentner, R.P., Johnson, E.N., Kutcher, H.R., and McConkey, B.J. 2008. Effect of glyphosate on Fusarium root infection of pea crops grown in rotation with spring wheat in the semi-arid Canadian prairies. Agri-Food Canada.

39. Fernandez, M.R., Zentner, R.P., Basnyat, P., Gehl, D., Selles, F., and Huber, D.M. 2009. Glyphosate associations with cereal diseases caused by Fusarium spp. in the Canadian Prairies. European J. Agron. 31:133-143.

40. Gabrielle, M.L. and Barriuso, E. 2008. Measurement and modeling of glyphosate fate compared with that of

herbicides replaced as a result of the introduction of glyphosate-resistant oilseed rape. Pest Manage. Sci. 64:262-275.

41.a. Gaines, T.A., Zhang, W., Wang, D., Bukun, B., Chisholm, S.T., Shaner, D.L., Nissen, S.J., Patzoldt, W.L., Tranel, P.J., Culpepper, S., Grey, T.L., Webster, T.M., Vencili, W.K., Sammons, R.D., Jiang, J., Preston, C., Leach, J.E., and Westra, P. 2010. Gene amplification confers glyphosate resistance in Amaranthus palmeri. PNAS 107:1029-1034.

42.   Ganson, R.J. and Jensen, R.A. 1988. The essential role of cobalt in the inhibition of the cytosolic isozyme of 3-deoxy-D-arabino-heptulosonate-7-phosphate synthase from Nicotiana silvestris by glyphosate. Arch Biochem. Biophys. 260:85-93.

43.   Gasnier, C., Dumont, C., Benachour, N., Clair,E., Chagnon, M-C., and Seralini, G-E. 2009. Glyphosate-based herbicides are toxic and endocrine disruptors in human cell lines. Toxicology 262:184-191.

44.   Gasnier, C., Benachour, N., Clair, E., Travert, C., Langlois, F., Laurant, C., Decroixs-Laporte, C., and Seralini, G-E. 2010. Dig 1 protects against cell death provoked by glyposate-based herbicides in human liver cell lines. J. Occupat. Med. Toxicol. 5:29-30.

45.   Gillam, C. 2010. Special report: are regulators dropping the ball on biocrops? Reuters http://www.reuters.com/assets/print?aid=USTRE63C2A J20100413.

45.a. Glass, R.L. 1984. Metal complex formation by glyphosate. J. Agric Food Chem 32:1249-1253.

46. Gordon, W.B. 2006. Manganese nutrition of glyphosate-resistant and conventional soybeans. Better Crops 91:12-13.

47. Gordon, B. 2006. Manganese nutrition of glyphosate-resistant and conventional soybeans. Great Plains Soil Fertility Conf. Proc. Denver, CO, March 7-8, 2006:224-2/

48. Gordon, W.B. 2007. Does (the) glyphosate gene affect manganese uptake in soybeans? Fluid J. Early Spring:12-13.

48.a. Guiden, R.H. and Swanton, C.J. 2007. The fate of plant DNA in soil and water—implications for the DNA cycle. Pp 115-125. In: R.H. Guiden & C.J. Swanton (eds.) The First Decade of Herbicide-resistant Crops in Canada. Canadian Weed Science Society.

49. Hanson, L.E. 2010. Interaction of Rhizoctonia solani and Rhizopus stolonifer causing root rot of sugar beet. Plant Dis. 94:504-509.

50. Hartzler, B. 2010. Glyphosate-manganese interactions in RoundUp Ready soybean. Iowa State Univ. Weed Sci. www.weeds.iastate.edu/mgmt/2010/glymn.pdf.

51. Hernandez, A., Garcia-Plazaola, J.I., and Bacerril, J.M. 1999. Glyphosate effects on phenolic metabolism of nodulated soybean (Glycine max L. Merril). J. Agric. Food Chem. 47:2920-2925.

52. Hornby, D., Bateman, G.L., Gutteridge, R.J., Lucas, P., Osbourn, A.E., Ward, E., and Yarham, D.J. 1998. Take-all Disease of Cereals: A Regional Perspective. CAB International, Wallingford, UK.

53. Huber, D.M. 2010. Ag chemical and crop nutrient interactions—current update. Proc. Fluid Fert. Forum, Scottsdale, AZ February 14-16, 2010. Vol. 27. Fluid Fertilizer Foundation, Manhattan, KS.

54. Huber, D.M. and McKay-Buis, T.S. 1993. A multicomponent analysis of the take-all disease of cereals. Plant Dis. 77:437-447.

55. Huber, D.M., Leuck, J.D., Smith, W.C., and Christmas, E.P. 2004. Induced manganese deficiency in GM soybeans. North central Fert. Exten. Conf., November 2004, Des Moines, IA.

56. Huber, D.M., Cheng, M.W., Winsor, B.A. 2005. Association of severe Corynespora root rot of soybean with glyphosate-killed giant ragweed. Phytopathology 95:545.

57. Huber, D.M. and Haneklaus, S. 2007. Managing nutrition to control plant disease. Landbauforschung Volkenrode 57:4:313-322.

58. Johal, G.R. and Rahe, J.E. 1984. Effect of soilborne plant-pathogenic fungi on the herbicidal action of glyphosate on bean seedlings. Phytopathology 74:950-955.

59. Johal, G.S. and Rahe, J.E. 1988. Glyphosate, hypersensitivity and phytoalexin accumulation in the incompati-

ble bean anthracnose host-parasite interaction. Physiol. Mol. Plant Patho. 32:267-281.

60. Johal, G.R. and Rahe, J.E. 1990. Role of phytoalexins in the suppression of resistance of Phaseolus vulgaris to Colletotrichum lindemuthianum by glyphosate. Can. J. Plant Pathol. 12:225-235.

61. Johal, G.R. and Huber, D.M. 2009. Glyphosate effects on diseases of plants. European J. Agron. 31:144-152.

62. Johnson, W.G., Davis, V.M., Kruger, G.R., and Weller, S.C. 2009. Influence of glyphosate-resistant cropping systems on weed species shifts and glyphosate-resistant weed populations. European J. Agron. 31:162-172.

63. Johnson, W.G., White, M., and Nice, G. 2010. Glyphosate and foliar fertilizers. Purdue Extension Weed Sci, 4/13/2010. www.btny.purdue.edu/weedscience/.

64. Jolley et al., 2004. Nutritional and management related interactions with iron-deficiency stress response mechanisms. Soil Sci. Plant Nutr. 50:973-981.

65. Keen, N.T., Holliday, M.J., Yoshikawa, M. 1982. Effects of glyphosate on glyceollin production and the expression of resistance to Phytophthora megasperma f.sp. glycinea in soybean. Phytopathology 72:467-1470.

66. Kervan, C.L. 1980. Biological Transmutations. (ISBN 0-916508-47-1).

67. King, C.A., Purcell, L.C., and Vories, E.D. 2001. Plant growth and nitrogenase activity of glyphosate-tolerant

soybean in response to foliar glyphosate applications. Agron. J. 93:79-186.

68. Knight, C.J., Bailey, A.M., and Foster, G.D. 2010. Investigating Agrobacterium-mediated transformation of Verticillium albo-atrum on plant surfaces. PloS ONE 5(10):e13684):1-5. Doi:10.1371/journal.pone.0013684.

69. Kremer, R.J., Donald, P.A., Keaster, A.J., and Minor, H.C. 2000. Herbicide impact on Fusarium spp. and soybean cyst nematode in glyphosate-tolerant soybean. Agron. Abstr. P. 257.

70. Kremer, R.J., Means, N.E., and Kim, S. 2005. Glyphosate affects soybean root exudation and rhizosphere microorganisms. Inter. J. Environ. Anal. Chem. 85:1165-1174.

71. Kremer, R.J. and Means, N.E. 2009. Glyphosate and glyphosate-resistant crop interactions with rhizosphere microorganisms. European J. Agron. 31:153-161.

72. Laitinen, P., Ramo, S., and Simes, K. 2005. Glyphosate translocation from plants to soil—does this constitute a significant proportion of residues in soil? Plant Soil 300:51-60.

73. Lanen M., Lorenz, N., and Dick, R. 2009. The effects of glyphosate on soil microbial community structure and potassium dynamics. Proc. Soil Sci. Soc. America 2009, Pittsburgh.

74. Larsen, R.L., Hill, A.L., Fenwick, A., Kniss, A.R., Hanson, L.E., and Miller, S.D. 2006. Influence of glypho-

sate on Rhizoctonia and Fusarium root rot in sugar beet. Pest Manag. Sci. 62:1182-1192.

75. Laskawy, T. 2010. USDA downplays own scientist's research on ill effects of Monsanto herbicide. http://www.grist.org/article/usda-downplays-own-scientists-research-on-danger-of-roundup/PALL/print:

76. Levesque, C.A., Rahe, J.E., and Eaves, D.M. 1987. Effects of glyphosate on Fusarium spp.: its influence on root colonization of weeds, propagule density in the soil, and crop emergence. Canadian J. Microbiol. 33:354-360.

77. Levesque, C.A. and Rahe, J.E. 1992. Herbicide interactions with fungal root pathogens, with special reference to glyphosate. Ann. Rev. Phytopathol. 30:579-602.

78. Levesque, C.A., Rahe, J.E., and Eaves, D.M. 1993. Fungal colonization of glyphosate treated seedlings using a new root plating technique. Mycol. Res. 97:299-306.

79. Liu, L., Punja, Z.K., and Rahe, J.E. 1995. Effect of Pythium spp. and glyphosate on phytoalexin production and exudation by bean (Phaseolus vulgaris L.) roots grown in different media. Physiol. Mol. Plant Pathol. 47:391-405.

80. Liu, L., Punja, Z.K. and Rahe, J.E. 1997. Altered root exudation and suppression of induced lignification as mechanisms of predisposition by glyphosate of bean roots (Phaseolus vulgaris L.) to colonization by Pythium spp. Physiol. Mol. Plant Pathol. 51:111-127.

81. Lorenz, N., Wojno, M., and Dick, R.P. 2008. Are soil microbial community composition and soil microbial potassium in glyphosate treated no-till soils linked to corn potassium deficiency? Proc. Soil Sci. Soc. America, 2008, Houston.

82. Lorenz, N. Wojno, M., and Dick, R. 2009. Soil microbial community composition and microbial biomass potassium in no-till soils under K deficient glyphosate-tolerant corn and soybean. Proc. Soil Sci. Soc. America 2009, Pittsburgh.

83. Lundager, Madsen et al. 1978. Stability constants of copper, zinc, manganese, calcium and magnesium complexes of glyphosate. Acta Chemica Scandinavica A 32:79-83.

84. Martell, A.E. and Smith, R.M. 1974. Critical Stability Constants. Plenum Press, New York. Vol. 1, 5 (first supplement), 6 (second supplement).

85. Mazza, R., Soave1,M., Morlacchini M., Piva, G., Marocco, A. (2005) Assessing the transfer of genetically modified DNA from feed to animal tissues, Transgenic Res. 14: 775-784.

85.a. McAfee, K. 2003. Neoliberalism on the molecular scale. Economica and genetic reductionism in biotechnology battles. Geoforum 34 (2003):203-219.

86. McDonald, D. 2001. Testimony before the Senate Agriculture Committee July, 2001, Washington, D.C.

87. Means, N.E., Kremer, R.J., and Ramsier, C. 2007. Effects of glyphosate and foliar amendments on activity of microorganisms in the soybean rhizosphere. J. Environ. Sci. Health Part B 42:125-132.

88. Mekwatanakarn, P. and Sivasithamparam, K. 1987. Effect of certain herbicides on soil microbial populations and their influence on saprophytic growth in soil and pathogenicity of the take-all fungus. Biol. Fertil. Soils 5;175-180.

89. Mensink, H. et al., 1994. Glyphosate. Environmental Health Criteria 59. World Health, Geneva.

90. Miller, M. 2010. Round up safer version of glyphosates. The Gazette: March 20, 2010.

91. Motavalli, P.P., Kremer, R.J., Fang, M., and Means, N.E. 2004. Impact of genetically modified crops and their management on soil microbially mediated plant nutrient transformations. J. Environ. Qual. 33:816-824.

92. Motekaitis and Martell, 1985. Metal chelate formation by N-phosphonomethyl glycine and related ligands. J. Coordination Chem. 14:139-149.

93. Neumann, G., Kohls, S., Landsberg, E., Stock-Olivera Souza, K., Yamada, T., and Roemheld, V. 2006. Relevance of glyphosate transfer to non-target plants via the rhizosphere. J. Plant Dis. Prot. 20:963-969.

94. Nilsson, G. 1985. Interactions between glyphosate and metals essential for plant growth. In: Grossbard E. and

Atkinson, D. (eds.) The Herbicide Glyphosate. Butter-worth, London. Pp 35-47.

95. Ostendorf, M. 2010. Are we shooting ourselves in the foot with a silver bullet? No-Till Farmer, March 2010:6-7.

96. Ozturk, L., Yazici, A., Eker, S., Gokmen, O., Roem-held, V., and Cakmak, I. 2008. Glyphosate inhibition of ferric reductase activity in iron deficient sunflower roots. New Phytol. 177:899-906.

97. Paganelli, A., Gnazzo, V., Acosta, H., Lopez, S.L., and Carrasco, A.E. 2010. Glyphosate-based herbicides produce teratogenic effects on vertebrates by impairing retinoic acid signaling. Chem. Res. Toxicol., August 9. http://pubs.acs.org/doi/abs/10.1021/tx1001749.

98. Powell, J.R. and Swanton, C.J. 2008. A critique of studies evaluating glyphosate effects on diseases associated with Fusarium spp. Weed Research 48:307-318.

99. Ptaszynski, B. and Zwolinska, A. 2001. Synthesis and properties of solid complexes of lanthanum, cerium, neodymium and erbium with N-phosphonomethyl glycine. Polish J. Environ. Studies 10:4:257-262.

100. Purcell, L.C., King, C.A., and Ball, R.A. 2000. Soybean cultivar differences in ureides and the relationship to drought tolerant nitrogen fixation and manganese nutrition. Crop Sci. 40:1062-1070.

101. Purcell, L.C. 2001. Physiological determinants of soybean yield limitations. USDA-CRIS Accession No.: 0164131; project No. ARK01559, Univ. Arkansas, Fayetteville.

101.a. Pusztai, A., Bardocz, S., and Ewen, S.W.B. 2003. Genetically modified foods: potential human health effects. Pp. 347-372. In: J.P.F. D'Mello0 (ed.) Food Safety: Contaminants and Toxins. CAB International, London.

101.b. Pusztai, A. and Bardocz, S. 2007. Potential health effects of foods derived from genetically modified plants: what are the issues. In: T. Traavik and L.L. Ching (eds.). Biosafety First—Holistic Approaches to Risk and Uncertainty in Genetic Engineering and Genetically Modified Organisms. Tapir Academic Press, Trndheim.

102. Pusztai, A. and Bardocz, S. 2007. Potential Health Effects of Foods Derived from Genetically Modified Plants: What are the issues. TwinIn: In: TWN Biotechnology & Biosafety Series 14. TWN, Third World Network, Penang, Malaysia. [reprinted from: Biosafety First—Holostic Approaches to Risk and Uncertainty in Genetic Engineering and Genetically Modified Organisms, 2007, Terje Traavik and Lim Li Ching (eds), Tapir Academic Press, Trondheim, ISBN: 9788251921138].

103. Pusztai, A. and Bardocz, S. 2010. Potential Health Effects of Foods Derived from Genetically Modified Plants: What Are the Issues? Third World Network, Malaysia.

103.a. Pusztai, A. and Bardocz, S. 2011. Potential Health Effects of Foods Derived from Genetically Modified Plants: What Are the Issues. TWN Biotechnology and Biosafety Series 14. Third World Network, Penang, Malaysia. 50 pp.

104. Rahe, J.E., Levesque, C.A., and Johal, G.S. 1990. Synergistic role of soil fungi in the herbicidal efficacy of glyphosate. In: Hoagland, R.E. (Ed.). Biological Weed Control Using microbes and Microbial Products as Herbicides. Symposium. April, April 9-14, 1989. American Chemical Society, Washington, DC, pp. 260-275.

105. Ran,T, Mei, L., Lei, W., Aihua, L., Ru, H., Jie, S. 2009. Detection of transgenic DNA in tilapias (Oreochromis niloticus, GIFT strain) fed genetically modified soybeans (RoundUp Ready). Aquaculture Research, Volume 40 (12): 1350-1357.

106. Reddy, K.N., Hoagland, R.E., and Zablotowicz, R.M. 2000). Effect of glyphosate on growth, chlorophyll, and nodulation in glyphosate-resistant and susceptible soybean (Glycine max) varieties. J. New Seeds 2:37-52.

107. Reddy, K.N. and Zablotowicz, R.M. 2003. Glyphosate-resistant soybean response to various salts of glyphosate and glyphosate accumulation in soybean nodules. Weed Sci. 51:496-502.

108. Reddy, K.N., Rimando, A.M., and Duke, S.O. 2004. Aminomethylphosphonic acid, a metabolite of glyphosate, causes injury in glyphosate-treated, glyphosate-resistant soybean. J. Agric. Food Chem. 52:5139-5143.

109. Reichenberger, L. 2007. Missing micronutrients: Using glyphosate is complicating the uptake of some minor nutrients. The Furrow Spring 2007:27-28.

110. Reimer, M., Farenhorst, A., and Gaultier, J. 2005. Effect of manure on glyphosate and trifluralin mineralization in soil. J. Environ. Sci. Health Part B, 40:605-617.

111. Rodrigues, J.J.V., Worsham, A.D., and Corbin, F.T. 1982. Exudation of glyphosate from wheat (Triticum aestivum) plants and its effects on interplanted corn (Zea mayes) and soybean (Glycine max). Weed Tech. 30:316-320.

112. Sanogo, S. , Yang, X.B., and Scherm, H. 2000. Effects of herbicides on Fusarium solani f.sp. glycines and development of sudden death syndrome in glyphosate-tolerant soybean. Phytopathology 90:57-66.

113. Sanogo, S., Yang, X.B. and Lundeen, P. 2001. Field response of glyphosate-tolerant soybean to herbicides and sudden death syndrome. Plant Dis. 85:773-779.

114. Schafer, J.R., Westhoven, A.M., Kruger, G.R., Davis, V.M., Hallett, S.G., and Johnson, W.G. 2009. Effect of growth media on common lambsquarters and giant ragweed biotypes response to glyphosate. Proc. North Central Weed Sci. Soc. 64:102.

115. Schafer, J.R, Hallett, S.G., and Johnson, W.G. 2010. Role of soil-borne fungi in the response of giant ragweed (Ambrosia trifida) biotypes to glyphosate. Proc. Northcentral Weed Sci. Soc. 65.

116. Schefers, J. 2011. Fetal and Perinatal mortalities associated with manganese deficiency. Minnesota Dairy health Conference. May 17-19, 2011. St. Paul, MN. University of Minnesota College of veterinary Medicine.

117. Schubbert, R., Hohlweg, U., Renz, D., Doerfler, W. (1998) On the fate of orallyingested foreign DNA in mice: chromosomal association and placental transmission to the fetus, Molecular Genetics Genomics 259: 569-576.

118. Seralini, G.E., Vendomois, J.S., Cellier, D., sultan, C., Buiatti, M., Gallagher, L., Antoniou, M., Dronamraju, K.R. 2009. How subchronic and chronic health effects can be negrected for GMOs, pesticides or chemicals. 2009. Int. J. Biol. Sci. 5:438-443.

119. Seralini, G-E., de Vendomois, J.S., Cellier, D., Mesnage, R. and Clair, E. 2010. Genetically modified crop consumption at large scale: Possible negative health impacts due to holes in assessment. Overview of the safety studies of GMOs performed on mammals. Pp 28-30. In: Breckling, B. and Verhoeven, R. 2010. Implications of GM-Crop Cultivation at large Spatial Scales. Theorie in der Okologie 16. Frankfurt, Perter Lang.

120. Seralini, G-E, Mesnage, R., Clair, E., Gress, S., de Vendomois, J.S., and Cellier, D. 2011. Genetically modified crops safety assessments: present limits and possible improvements. Environ. Sci. Europe 23:10-20. http://www.enveurope.com/content/23/1/10.

121. Severson, R. 2006. Influence of RoundUp herbicide on manganese nutrition of soybean. http://www.nwroc.umn.edu/Cropping_Issues/NW_Crop _trials/2005/Sybn_glyph_+_manganese.pdf.

122. Sharma, R., Damgaard, D., Alexander, T.W., Dugan, M.E.R., Aalhus, J.L., Stanford, K., McAllister, T.A. (2006) Detection of transgenic and endogenous plant DNA in tissues of sheep and pigs fed RoundUp Ready canola meal. Journal of Agricultural Food Chemistry 54: 1699–1709.

123. Smiley, R.W., Ogg, A.G., and Cook, R.J. 1992. Influence of glyphosate on Rhizoctonia root rot, growth, and yield of barley. Plant Dis. 76:937-942.

124. Tesfamariam, T., Bott, S., Cakmak, I., Roemheld, V., and Neumann, G. 2009. Glyphosate in the rhizosphere—role of waiting times and different glyphosate binding forms in soils for phytoxicity to non-target plants. European J. Agron. 31:126-132.

125. Tudisco, R., Mastellone, V., Cutrignelli1, M.I, Lombardi, P, Bovera1F., Mirabella, N., Piccolo1, G., Calabro1, S., Avallone, L., Infascelli, F. 2010. Fate of transgenic DNA and evaluation of metabolic effects in goats fed genetically modified soybean and in their off-springs.

126. United States Patent Office. 1964. Aminomethyle-nephosphinic acids, salts thereof, and process for their production. Patent No. 3,160,632, Dec. 8. 1964.

127. de Vendomois, J.S., Roullier, F., Cellier, D., and Ser-
     alini, G-E. 2009. A comparison of the effects of three
     GM corn varieties on mammalian health. Int. J. Biol.
     Sci. 5:706-726.

128. Wagner, R., Kogan, M., and Parada, M. 2003. Phyto-
     toxic activity of root absorbed glyphosate in corn seed-
     lings (Zea mays L.) Weed Biol. Manag.3:228-232.

129. Walsh, L.P., McCormick, C., Martin, C. and Stocco,
     D.M. 2000. RoundUp inhibits steroidogenesis by dis-
     rupting steroidogenic acute regulatory (StAR) proetein
     expression. Environ. Health Perspec. 108:769-776.

130. Waltz, E. 2009. Battlefield; Papers suggesting that bio-
     tech crops might harm the environment attract a hail of
     abuse from other scientists. Nature 461/3:27-32.

131. Yamada, T., Kremer, R.J., Camargo e Castro, P.R., and
     Wood, B.W. 2009. Glyphosate interactions with physi-
     ology, nutrition, and diseases of plants: Threat to agri-
     cultural sustainability? European J. Agron. 31:111-113.

132. Yang, Y. 2010. In situ and ex situ effects of glyphosate
     on the soil microbial community. http://a-c-
     s.confex.com/crops/2010am/webprogram/paper58781.ht
     ml.

133. Zablotowicz, R.M. and Reddy, K.N. 2007. Nitrogenase
     activity, nitrogen content, and yield responses to gly-
     phosate in glyphosate-resistant soybean. Crop Prot.
     26:370-376.

134. Zobiole, L.H.S., Oliveira,, R.S. Jr., Kremer, R.J., Constantin, J., Yamada, T. Castro, C. Oliveira, F.A., and Oliveira, A. Jr.. 2010. Effect of glyphosate on symbiotic N2 fixation and nickel concentration in glyphosate-resistant soybeans. Appl. Soil Ecol. 44:176-180.

135. Zobiole, L.H.S., Oliveira, R.S. Jr., Huber, D.M., Constantin, J., Castro, C., Oliveira, F.A., Oliveira, A. Jr. 2010. Glyphosate reduces shoot concentrations of mineral nutrients in glyphosate-resistant soybeans. Plant Soil 328:57-69.

136. Zobiole, L.H.S., Oliveira, R.S. Jr., Kremer, R.J., Constantin, J., Bonato, C.M., and Muniz, A.S. 2010. Water use efficiency and photosynthesis as affected by glyphosate application to glyphosate-resistant soybean. Pesticide Biochem. Physiol. 97:182-193.

137. Zobiole, L.H.S., Bonini, E.A., Oliveira, R.S. Jr., Kremer, R.J., and Ferrarese-Filho, O. 2010. Glyphosate affects lignin content and amino acid production in glyphosate-resistant soybean. Acta Physiol. Plant. 32:831-837.

138. Zobiole, L.H.S., Oliveira, Jr., R.S., Kremer, R.J., Muniz, A.S., and Oliveira Jr., A. 2010. Nutrient accumulation and photosynthesis in glyphosate resistant soybeans is reduced under glyphosate use. J. Plant Nutr. 33:1860-1873.

139. Zobiole, L.H.S., Oliveira Jr., Constantin, J., R.S., Kremer, R.J., Biffe, D.F. 2010. Amino application can be an alternative to prevent glyphosate injury. J. Plant Nutr. (In Press).

140. Zobiole, L.H.S., Oliveira Jr., Visentainer, J.V., Kremer, R.J., Yamada, T., Bellaloui, N. 2010. Glyphosate affects seed composition in glyphosate-resistant soybean. J. Agric. Food chem..58:4517-4522.

141. Zobiole, L.H.S., Kremer, R.J., Oliveira, R.S., and Constantin, J. 2010. Glyphosate affects rhizosphere microorganisms of "first and second generation" glyphosate-resistant soybeans (Glycine max). J. Appl. Microbiol. 110:118-127.

142. Zobiole, L. H. S., Kremer, R.J., Oliveira Jr., R. S. and Constantin, J. 2010. Glyphosate affects photosynthesis in first and second generation of glyphosate-resistant soybeans.. Plant and Soil 336:251-265.

143. Zobiole, L. H. S., Kremer, R.J., Oliveira Jr., R. S. and Constantin, J. 2011. Glyphosate affects chlorophyll, nodulation and nutrient accumulation of "second generation" glyphosate-resistant soybean (Glycine max L.). Pesticide Biochemistry and Physiology. 99:53-60.

144. Zobiole, L.H.S.; Oliveira Jr., R.S.; Constantin, J. and Biffe, D.F. 2011. Prevention of RR soybean injuries caused by exogenous supply of aminoacids. Planta daninha [online]. 2011, vol.29, n.1, pp. 195-205. ISSN 0100-8358.

    Glyphosate-resistant (RR) soybean crop areas have expanded every year. However, as a result of this expansion, the use of glyphosate has significantly increased, with the appearance of visual injuries in RR soybeans immediately after post-emergence application of the herbicide. Thus, two experiments were conducted in different years with different objectives. The first experiment aimed to evaluate the influence of glyphosate on photosynthetic variables and biomass production.

The second experiment aimed to re-evaluate the same parameters affected in RR soybeans by glyphosate, as well as the use of various methods of amino acid application, as a form of a likely recovery of the soybean plants following these exogenous applications. The photosynthetic rate and SPAD index decreased as the glyphosate rate increased, with a pronounced decrease after a single herbicide application. Overall, due to a decrease in the photosynthetic rate and chlorophyll production, as well as to a likely immobilization of shoot nutrient concentration by glyphosate, a significant biomass decrease was verified in the treatments with glyphosate application. However, the use of exogenous amino acids may be a strategy to safeguard the undesirable effects of this herbicide on RR soybean.

145. Zobiole, L.H.S. et al. Use of exogenous amino acid to prevent glyphosate injury in glyphosate-resistant soybean. Planta daninha [online]. 2010, vol.28, n.3, pp. 643-653. ISSN 0100-8358. doi: 10.1590/S0100-83582010000300022.

Cultivation of glyphosate-resistant (GR) soybeans has increased in Brazil as a result of the application of this technology in weed management systems developed for this crop. However, the expansion of GR soybean production has significantly increased the use of glyphosate and, in some cases, resulted in injury symptoms observed in GR soybean, known as "yellow flashing" or yellowing of the upper leaves. Thus, two experiments were conducted in different years.

The first experiment aimed to evaluate the influence of glyphosate on GR soybeans regarding the photosynthetic variables, nodule parameters, and shoot and root dry biomass by comparing cultivar BRS 242 GR without glyphosate and BRS 242 RR + glyphosate at 1.200 g ha-1 at V4 growth stage, to the near isogenic non-GR parental line cv. Embrapa 58. The second experiment aimed to reassess the same parameters in GR soybeans at the V4 stage treated with glyphosate, plus the application of various amino acids, to evaluate the expected recovery of soybean growth under the exogenous use of supplemental amino acids. In general, the photosynthetic variables, nodulation parameters and shoot and root dry biomass were affected by glyphosate; however, the use of amino acids may be a strategy to prevent the undesirable effects of this herbicide on GR soybean.